HAUNTINGS

Abhirup Dhar is a Kolkata-born, bestselling author of books such as, *Once Again...With Love!, Stories Are Magical, Hold That Breath!, The Belvoirbrooke Haunting, Hold That Breath 2* and *Ghost Hunter, Gaurav Tiwari: The Life and Legacy of India's Foremost Paranormal Investigator*. Dhar's writing has been endorsed by the renowned film-makers Vikram Bhatt and Sunil Bohra, who also acquired the screen rights for *Ghost Hunter, Gaurav Tiwari*. Dhar also writes movie scripts with reputed film-makers. A recipient of various awards and honours, Dhar has been called by *Mid-Day* as the most acclaimed name in Indian horror writing.

Indian Paranormal Society (IPS) was founded by Gaurav Tiwari in 2009. It has been a pioneer in metaphysical/anomalous research around the globe, especially in India. The collective gained popularity in the field of paranormal research because of the investigations they handled by travelling to different parts of the country. IPS aims to shun myths and superstitions about the paranormal through logical evaluation, critical thinking and applying principles of forensic science. IPS has helped thousands get rid of their fear of the unknown by spreading awareness about this field.

You can reach Indian Paranormal Society at:
Website: https://indianparanormalsociety.in/
E-mail: indianparanormalsociety@gmail.com
Facebook: www.facebook.com/indianparanormalsociety
YouTube: www.youtube.com/gripindia
Twitter: https://twitter.com/GRIPOfficial02?s=09
Instagram: https://www.instagram.com/indian_paranormal_society0209/

HAUNTINGS

Stories Based on
Actual Paranormal Investigations

Abhirup Dhar with
Indian Paranormal Society

RUPA

Published by
Rupa Publications India Pvt. Ltd 2022
7/16, Ansari Road, Daryaganj
New Delhi 110002

Sales centres:
Prayagraj Bengaluru Chennai
Hyderabad Jaipur Kathmandu
Kolkata Mumbai

P-ISBN: 978-93-5520-632-9
E-ISBN: 978-93-5520-633-6

Second impression 2023

10 9 8 7 6 5 4 3 2

*Dedicated to Reverend Gaurav Tiwari,
beloved friend, son, brother and
CEO/founder of the Indian Paranormal Society*

Contents

A Note on Gaurav Tiwari

Reverend Gaurav Tiwari (2 September 1984–7 July 2016) was the CEO and founder of Indian Paranormal Society (IPS) and the director of Ghost Research and Investigators of the Paranormal Academy. He went to Florida to fulfil his aspiration of becoming a certified commercial pilot. He successfully completed the training programme and was presented with a commercial pilot license. During his time in Florida, where he stayed in a shared rental apartment with his batchmates from his flying school, he experienced some inexplicable things. Until then, he had neither believed in ghosts nor had he been aware of the paranormal. However, these experiences made him research the topic and join the Paranexus Anomalous Research Association to earn his degree in metaphysical/paranormal research.

Rev. Tiwari became a certified lead paranormal investigator and a Paranexus representative in India. He had a Bachelor of Metaphysical Humanistic Science degree and was a certified paranormal investigator and a certified UFO field investigator. Along with being an ordained minister (reverend) of the Metaphysical Church of Humanistic Science, Florida, Rev. Tiwari was a certified hypnotist and past life regression practitioner from the same institution. He trained to be a spiritual counsellor and life/relationship coach from the Institute of Metaphysical Humanistic Science. Rev. Tiwari's guru Dr Doug Kelley, founder and president of the Paranexus Anomalous Research Association, enabled him to achieve these feats.

Upon returning to India in 2009, he established IPS—India's first professional paranormal team, which brought him international repute. He featured on different television shows in India, promoting paranormal/metaphysical research while making it entertaining and accessible. He featured as a paranormal researcher or expert on *MTV Girls Night Out* hosted by Rannvijay Singha, MTV's *Haunted Weekends with Sunny Leone* and *He Ticket*, Zee TV's *Fear Files*, Sony TV's *Bhoot Aaya,* SyFy's *Haunting: Australia* and various other shows. He also featured on different news channels such as, Aaj Tak, India TV, News 24, Star TV, Zee News, IBN7, etc. Rev. Tiwari was also invited to famous international paranormal radio shows. He and his team earned an international reputation after busting the myth of Bhangarh.

Introduction

Looking at the current scene of paranormal research in India, the one thing that stands out is the way it is depicted in movies. Although paranormal research has existed since the nineteenth century, there has never been a case where the subject of research—i.e., the 'spirit/ghost', as laypersons know it—has been spotted wearing a white gown with twisted legs and a candle in its hand. We could say that these images are a by-product of man's wildest imagination. Such depictions actually act as hurdles by creating an irrational fear among people or maybe by making people doubt the existence of the paranormal.

India has also seen a rising trend of godmen over the years. People worship and approach them in times of need. People actually believe that these godmen have supernatural powers, but when it comes to accepting the fact that a particular place is actually haunted by energies (spirits), they find it difficult to digest. Furthermore, there are a lot of misconceptions about the paranormal in people's minds. If we were to name the number of 'ghosts' that the people of India have come across, it might take us an entire day to jot them down. However, as Rev. Tiwari used to rightly say, 'Knowledge cancels fear'. If people are properly educated about what this area of research is all about, we believe that, one day, everyone might possibly accept this parallel reality.

It's important for people to understand that there is not enough money to be made in the field of paranormal investigation in India—not enough to make a living for sure. It's a different matter that the passion to explore the unknown is what holds the IPS team together. Furthermore, they take up cases to help people who require it, but someone thinking of pursuing paranormal investigation as a full-time profession must reconsider their decision. Gaurav used to run the show really well and was extensively covered by the media, which also helped bring legitimacy to the profession. But, when it came to money matters, he faced a very difficult time sustaining the model. Clients mostly pay for the travel expenses and take care of the lodging, but the price for the services rendered is low. At times, Gaurav got some help from sponsors, which kept him moving, but the rent of the Delhi office and various other costs burdened him. The office was shut down after he passed away and Raj, one of the IPS team members, planned the way ahead for them—a rather low-cost model, where the team would basically operate from their homes whenever required.

Professionalism is one of the many things Gaurav inculcated in himself and his team. He always told his team members that they are the face of paranormal investigation in India and their work will be discussed in international forums, too. They should always represent the field well, as it is much ridiculed in India. Many perceive paranormal investigators to be frauds who try to impose misleading supernatural theories on their clients. So, it is important to focus only on the work and be well-groomed, well-mannered and always reach a venue before time, while at it, without paying attention to the naysayers. IPS still believes in letting their work speak for themselves. You will never find them craving for attention by doing unnecessary activities, and people still reckon with IPS when it comes to paranormal investigation in India. The trust and goodwill bestowed upon their work is a result of many years of hard work, patience, perseverance and unflinching faith in determining the truth using the most scientific approach. A professional investigation conducted by the IPS includes the following phases[*]:

1. Client interview, where the client speaks to us and states what they are experiencing in their property. We also ask a few other questions and perform a small client screening session to determine if the case really requires our intervention/professional paranormal investigation and rule out any possibility of foul play. During this phase, we also send the clients a few forms, like non-

---

[*]The complete details of all the phases have not been provided in this note to retain the elements of suspense in the narrative of the cha⌐

disclosures/expectations form, permission to investigate, client assumption of risk and initial contact/interview form to collect the client's data, like the history of the place, the nature of the paranormal experiences, a list of members who have experienced the paranormal activity, family members/people who stay at the place, etc.

2. We visit the location to conduct a preliminary investigation, which involves a quick investigation of the property. The moment we step in, we note down the readings displayed on our equipment (electromagnetic frequency [EMF]/K-II meters) to see if we get any unusual readings during normal conditions (first, with all the electrical equipment, like fans, tube lights, etc. switched on and subsequently, with everything switched off). We also use these as our baseline readings before starting the third phase, which is conducting a full-fledged paranormal investigation. Later, we refer back to our baseline readings to compare the new readings and the real time readings that we document on our equipment.

3. We conduct a proper investigation by setting up high-end equipment, like night vision cameras, motion sensors, EMF meters, infrared video cameras, DSLR cameras, etc., in the place of investigation to document any evidence or subtle changes in the ambient environment. The goal here is not to prove anything but to observe and document any changes. During the observation, if we experience anything unusual at a certain spot within the property, we mark it as a 'hotspot' and try

to focus majorly on that place to see if the anomaly recurs when a different researcher looks into it, or if we can document anything substantial that may explain the client's experience. This phase may, depending on our experience during the investigation, involve client counselling, where we ensure that the collective experience of the client and the investigators doesn't negatively impact the client's psychology. This process aims to empower the client to be self-reliant and not fall prey to frauds done by self-proclaimed godmen, which may impact them negatively.

4. Next, we sit down to analyse the recordings and documentation to check if we have caught something on our equipment. If we have managed to document something that, we feel, may be significant evidence of the paranormal, we attempt to rationalize and debunk it, thereby ruling out any normal occurrences (sounds from stray dogs, people talking in the background, an EMF spike due to mobile phones, etc.), the things that may be caused by something natural or a contamination (caused by us or any technical or man-made error). If we come across a piece of documentation that passes all the tests (debunking/rationalizing), we clip and save it to share it with the client. If we don't document anything unusual or something significant, we inform the client and close the case.

5. This step is optional and completely depends on what we come across during the fourth phase of evidence analysis.

We revisit the property and conduct a short preliminary investigation to check if our experiences from the third phase can be repeated. This stage also involves us performing a cleansing session. Different teams cleanse differently. We usually communicate with whatever entity is present in that space and see if we can help the intelligence in a way that it stops appearing before the clients. We ensure this through a small investigation and using our experience from the third phase as reference to check if we document anything unusual.

6. We counsel the members of the family. The main purpose of this counselling session is to help the clients overcome their fears of the unknown and strengthen their belief system. Also, in this phase, we showcase and explain all the evidence that we have documented during the investigation.

The stories in this book are based on actual paranormal investigations conducted by IPS, which was founded by Rev. Gaurav Tiwari, the pioneer of paranormal investigation in India, in 2009. A spiritual sequel to *Ghost Hunter: Gaurav Tiwari* (Westland, 2021), this book is a fictionalized account of how IPS came out strong to live Gaurav's dream and vision after his mysterious and shocking death in 2016. The names, locations and all personal details of the clients, whose cases these stories are loosely based on, have been fictionalized, and these clients have permitted IPS to do so for the book.

In conclusion, we would like to clarify that the intent

of writing this book is not to scare readers but to make you aware of the field of paranormal investigation while telling you about a few of the choicest cases investigated by IPS after Rev. Tiwari's death.

Prologue

It was Siddharth's first night in Delhi, training under his mentor, Rev. Gaurav Tiwari. There was a lot of work that night, and, moreover, he hadn't finalized a rented accommodation yet. So, he decided to sleep in the IPS office in Dwarka after everyone left. The young, passionate man was happy because ever since he had joined the IPS, he had wanted to be mentored by Gaurav; not just through calls and a few meetings but by staying with him, observing him, learning from the man himself.

Gaurav had got the office on rent, not very far from his home in Dwarka, along the western fringes of Delhi. The space had been a psychiatric clinic before it shut down and the owner decided to let it out again. It was a wonderful place that Gaurav and his team members were very fond of and referred to as a creative den. People who visited the office also got nice vibes and left the space content with the help of the IPS members, who usually offered them a practical and feasible solution after investigating the haunted locations. For Siddharth, his mentor's presence in the office made him even more motivated and energetic. But, there was more to the office than met the eye.

Siddharth's experiences had begun the afternoon he joined, but he had been doubtful about them then. He had been seated on a sofa in the waiting room when he had noticed a shadow-like figure move into the kitchen. He had stood up and walked inside, but no one had been there. He had looked out of the window. Nobody.

'All good? Looking for something?', Gaurav asked, tapping Siddharth's shoulder, bringing him back from his reverie.

Siddharth recounted his experience from the afternoon to Gaurav, who responded, 'You are either overthinking or you must be really tired. Get some sleep tonight.'

Siddharth decided to do just that. However, just when he was about to doze off, he heard some noise coming from the kitchen. The lights were still on and he was alone. Before he left, Gaurav had instructed Siddharth to lock the doors and close the windows properly; Gaurav had also asked another team member to stay with Siddharth, but that member had refused.

'Who could it be?' Siddharth wondered, getting up to listen carefully.

Siddharth could clearly hear the sound in the kitchen— it sounded like someone was crushing an empty plastic bottle. He switched on all the lights, checked every nook and corner of the office, but he did not find anybody and anything peculiar.

'Could it be that I'm hearing things?' he mumbled to himself and went back to bed.

A few minutes later, he started hearing the noises again and, this time, there were voices—the kind of chaos and commotion one hears in a crowded place. The intensity of the noise grew gradually till the point that Siddharth had to put his hands over his ears to muffle the sound. He stood up again, opened the main door and looked out at the rather quaint residential neighbourhood where everyone seemed to be fast asleep. Evidently, Siddharth couldn't sleep that night.

The next day, he discussed his experience with Gaurav as soon as he came to office.

'Look, Siddharth,' Gaurav said with a sigh, offering him a glass of water. 'First, sit down and breathe,' he instructed, calmly, sitting across from Siddharth. 'I know what is going on here,' Gaurav said.

'What?' Siddharth asked shocked. Why had Gaurav not told him about this earlier?

'Don't look surprised! I just didn't want you to be psychologically affected or get scared. There is no other reason behind not telling you this.'

Gaurav explained that Siddharth wasn't the only one experiencing something unnatural in the office. The team member who had refused to stay with him the previous night had also seen a child-like figure suddenly run across the hallway into the kitchen one evening. Another day, he had felt an ice-cold hand touch the back of his neck. On a hot and humid summer afternoon, the office boy had heard the doorbell ring. He had peeped out from the keyhole and seen someone waiting outside the door. Thinking it would be a client, he had opened the door, but nobody had been outside! He had even walked out to check, but not a single person had been around. One morning, as the same office boy had been preparing tea for a client waiting for Gaurav, he had heard someone call his name from Gaurav's cabin.

'Did you hear that too?', he had asked the client, shivering.

'No. What?' The client had stared blankly at the office boy, who had been at his wit's end.

After recounting these instances, Gaurav said, 'See, there was a psychiatric clinic here earlier, but I don't think that's much of a reason for these happenings. You never know, something may have followed me here.' Gaurav smiled reassuringly at Siddharth, who was going to stay in Delhi for a few months, which also meant that he would probe into the matter further till he was satisfied!

That night, after everyone left, Siddharth knew what to do—find out more about his experience. He set up his equipment, including his electronic voice phenomena (EVP) recorder, to ask questions and document answers. He was an expert in analysing audio anomalies. Though not much happened during the session, he managed to document what sounded like the voice of a little child. This evidence certainly backed up what he and a few others had experienced at the office.

Siddharth presented the evidence to Gaurav next morning. Gaurav listened to the anomaly a couple of times and tried to recollect if he had heard a similar voice in one of his many cases. There was a chance he had. So, he concluded, 'Like I had told you, something must have followed me here.'

Gaurav had a habit of collecting souvenirs during his investigations. After each case, he would bring something to his office. It could be something as small as a coin, but he just felt a sense of belonging because of it. After concluding an investigation, Gaurav would thank the entity and sometimes, even invite it to follow him out of the place so that the haunting would stop in that place.

Empathy towards life after death is something he believed in and taught his team to do so as well.

ONE

The Kashmir Ghost

It had been almost two months since Rev. Gaurav Tiwari had passed away—two months of mourning and missing a man everyone looked up to. He had been a mentor and a friend, in addition to being a great human being, who had made a mark by starting a movement to usher in paranormal investigation using an indisputable scientific approach for the first time in India. Gaurav had supposedly died by suicide on 7 July 2016. However, there had been other theories about his death, which the IPS didn't want to comment on. As per statements given by his family, Gaurav had been visiting a haunted house in Janakpuri for a few days before his death, and he had informed them that an evil spirit had latched on to him. The family had added that during a dinner-table conversation, Gaurav had attributed the deep black mark on his neck to spirits in distress trying to seek revenge. But, if one were to connect the dots, Gaurav might have been suffering from depression for various reasons. Mental health can be deceptive; a person may appear to be happy and content and may never disclose his internal suffering to anyone, no matter how close a person is to him or her.

Two days after Gaurav's birthday, Siddharth and Meghna called for an IPS team meeting in Mumbai. Mohan, one of the team members of IPS who maintains a very low profile, and Rith joined them in person while Raj joined them on Skype, as he couldn't travel from Delhi.

Meghna, the more mature and level-headed member of the team, spoke first, 'It has been a very tough phase, everyone. I know what Gaurav meant to each one of us and that void can never be filled. Never. But what we are doing is wrong,' she paused and realized that they were all emotional, like her. The team hadn't been together for a few months and still were in a state of shock and great despair. Siddharth had been in Delhi when Gaurav had passed away; he had informed Meghna over phone that night.

'We should get back to work,' Raj, who was among Gaurav's closest friends, asserted.

'Yes, guys. Gaurav would never want to see us like this. He wants us to live his dream and vision,' Siddharth said. Motivated by his team members, Raj sat up straight in his chair and narrated the tale he had recently heard.

∽

Newlywed couple, Ankush and Swati, were on their way to Pahalgam in Kashmir for their honeymoon. Theirs was an arranged marriage, although they had met a couple of times before tying the knot to be sure that they wanted to spend the rest of their lives together. Sparks had flown during their first date and they had known that, years later, they would tell their kids about their love story. Swati had noticed many of her father's habits in Ankush—a girl always looks for her father's qualities in her life partner. On the other hand, Ankush had thought that Swati was a very caring and intelligent person, something he had always wanted in his wife. Soon after, they had gotten married.

Ankush and Swati sat in the car they had taken from Srinagar airport, enjoying the scenery along the winding mountain path and looking forward to the week-long vacation. It was a little past two in the afternoon and they both were hungry.

'Can we stop at a restaurant on the way?' Ankush asked the driver.

'There are a few good ones near Pampore, which we will be crossing in a while, Sir. This restaurant I have in mind is in a rather deserted part but you will enjoy your meal,' the driver responded.

'Good, good. We are also looking for such places, away from the hustle and bustle of city life—less people, no pollution. What fresh air!' Ankush exclaimed with a smile and asked the driver to switch off the AC.

'Feel it!' Ankush told Swati and opened the car window at his side.

The fresh air and the greenery of the trees and shrubs came together in their own ballet dance. As the fresh mountain air filled their lungs, they felt a sense of calm. This was heaven already!

'We are here, Sir,' the driver said, shaking them out of their awestruck reverie, which was never possible in the city.

'Ah...let's go,' Ankush said, getting down and opening the door for Swati.

'It's a beautiful place!' Swati looked around and smiled, the twinkle in her eyes catching Ankush's attention.

'Don't miss the lip-smacking Wazwan dishes here, especially Rista Curry and Lahabi Kebab! Take your time, Sir. We have time,' the driver guided them.

'Thank you! People in Kashmir are really helpful,' Swati said as they proceeded towards the small and empty restaurant.

'*Waliv!* (Welcome!),' the restaurant owner greeted them with a wide smile.

The couple had a sumptuous meal, thanked the owner for his hospitality and decided to take a walk around; they wouldn't get to experience such wonderful environs when they returned to the humdrum of city life a few days later, so they wanted to make the most of every minute.

They walked towards a forested area just a stone's throw away from the restaurant. They felt a sense of kinship with the flora, an ancient soul that stretches into everything that lives. The sunrays filtered through the softened, verdant and freshly aromatic foliage, giving the place a more enchanting look; the roots of the ancient trees intertwined across the forest floor.

'They are right about Kashmir. *Agar kahi jannat hai, woh yehi hai* (if there is heaven anywhere, it is here),' Swati said to Ankush, holding his hand tightly and planting a soft kiss on his shoulder.

Every tree glowed brightly virescent just at the edges of the trunks, a biological halo of sorts that brought the couple a soothing happiness that they missed in the city. They decided to sit under one of the trees and spend some time together. In the centre of the innumerable trees stood one with a bark that had the pattern of rain-fed flash rivers. It stretched up, almost looking proud to stand there under the sun in any weather. How one wished the tree could see its own beauty—its green bounty and earthy browns!

'Such a beautiful place, Ankush! How can anything bad ever happen here?' Swati exclaimed, as they sat under the beautiful tree and kissed. In the kiss was the sweetness of waiting for real love, which Ankush had found in Swati. She knew that it was a relationship that, if nurtured well, would make a good example of great companionship—a woman can tell this by the way a man kisses her for the first time. While making out in the open empty space, they lost sense of time. Their lips fitted perfectly, as if they had always been meant for each other. They were moving against each other, feeling each other. Ankush grabbed the back of Swati's neck and she moaned in pleasure. In the split second before his touch, every nerve in Swati's body and brain had been electrified. It was probably the anticipation of being together in a way that's more than words, in a way that's so completely tangible.

'Kushal!' Ankush heard Swati say as she bit his ear.

'Ouch! Kushal, who?' Ankush held her back.

'Kushal?' Swati looked at him blankly.

'Yes. You just called me by that name,' Ankush said, furious. Could it be that Swati had had a lover before marriage, whom she never mentioned in the last few weeks of their courtship? Everyone has a past, but she could have told him.

'I don't know anyone by that name, Ankush,' she said and stood up, unhappy with the interruption to their intimate moment.

'Let's leave,' Ankush stood up too. He was sure he had heard his wife call him Kushal.

They reached the hotel late in the evening and checked into the cosy honeymoon suite. Swati sat down to explain things to Ankush.

'You must have misheard, baba! Come, I'll make up for it,' she said, smiling.

'But—'

She pressed her lips against his mid-sentence and he leaned back. Swati started unbuttoning his shirt, but he turned his head away.

'Are you sure you don't want to do it?' Swati asked.

Swati was in a mood for some mischief and continued kissing him until she got to his jeans. They undressed each other and took a bath in a Jacuzzi, making love until dinner was served. It was all okay again, or so they thought.

Around 3:00 a.m., Ankush woke up when he heard a strange sound, like someone scratching a concrete surface.

'Swati!' Ankush called out, but she was not in the bed.

Rubbing his eyes, he got out of the bed, wore his boxer shorts, put on his slippers, since the floor was colder than the air, and tried to switch on the dim lamp on the side table but couldn't.

'Power cut?' He mumbled and switched on his mobile flashlight and moved it around the room.

'Swati,' he called his wife again—a little louder this time. The sound stopped.

Ankush swept the light around the room again and saw his wife standing near the main door of the room, chanting something, maybe a name.

Ankush could hear her clearly as he stepped closer to her.

'Kushal. Kushal. Kushal. Kushal...' she kept saying, standing still and facing the door.

'Swati!' Ankush called out loudly.

Just then, the lights came on. Swati turned around to stare at her scared husband; his fear frightened her too. Something wrong had happened and she didn't quite know what it had been.

'Look!' he pointed to the door.

Swati had carved in big bold letters—KUSHAL—on the door. She screamed and threw away the sharp piece of wood she had in her hand.

'What is happening, Ankush?' she cried and hugged him.

Ankush didn't really know how he was supposed to react. Shocked. Scared. Doubtful. He was all of that and more. They packed their bags and went downstairs to the reception. It was empty.

'Is anybody here?' Ankush yelled.

'Y...yes,' A man came running from a nearby room, where the staff, perhaps, caught up with some sleep at night.

'We want to leave. NOW!' Ankush told him.

'Anything wrong, Sir?' the man asked, annoyed at being woken up from his slumber and being told this.

Ankush explained, stammering while he spoke, as he was very scared. The hotel attendant listened to him patiently.

The man paused for a few seconds before speaking, 'That place you went to near the restaurant—'

'Yes. What about it?' Ankush asked.

'It's jinxed, Sir. They say a couple died by suicide in that forest. Some others believe that they were murdered. Their bodies were found hanging from a tree one morning. This happened a few years ago.'

Ankush and Swati looked at each other in terror.

'Let's...let's just leave. I'm not feeling well,' Swati said softly.

∽

Ankush and Swati returned to Delhi after their miserable honeymoon thinking it would all be fine. They even

13

considered planning another trip soon, but Swati had to get well first. She was sick and slept for almost the entire day—at times she would even throw up blood. The family doctor visited Swati and conducted some tests, but he was unable to pinpoint the reason for her illness. The first four days after the couple returned from Kashmir were spent in looking after Swati; the entire family was very concerned and hadn't yet informed her parents, else they would have been very worried.

Every morning, Ankush's father used to slide out of his bed quietly, without disturbing his wife, and head to Nehru Park to exercise. He used to return by 6:00 a.m. and get ready for the day. On the fifth day after Ankush and Swati's return, an incident shook them all. At around 4:00 a.m., Ankush's father woke up for his daily walk. As he walked down the stairs to proceed towards the main door, he saw Swati seated on the sofa in the living room, staring blankly at the television, which was switched off.

'Swati, are you okay?' he asked softly as he came closer to his sick daughter-in-law.

No answer.

'Beta, it will all be okay. Don't worry. I'll get the best possible medical check-up for you.'

Still, no answer. Swati did not even bat an eyelid. She simply stared with open eyes, as if she was a statue.

'Swati...' Ankush's father said tentatively, feeling a chill run down his spine.

'Yes, Papa,' she replied, facing him with a smile. The

dark circles around her eyes were getting worse by the day.

'Are you okay?' he repeated.

'Papa, Kushal will be home today. Please hear him out patiently. Don't overreact,' she responded.

'Kush...al?'

'Papa, we can't live without each other. Really.'

'I don't—'

Ankush's father stopped halfway when he noticed the smile on Swati's face turn into a frown, her eyes gleaming red.

'Don't you dare touch him!' she shouted at him, her eyes bleeding.

'What?! Ankush! Ankush!', he called out, petrified. He had no clue what he should do.

They rushed Swati to a hospital immediately and called the family doctor. However, regardless of their decades-long relationship, even the family doctor was helpless this time. He had consulted various other doctors, but there just seemed to be no explanation for Swati's condition.

Swati was kept under observation for a day and then discharged.

Finally, Ankush mailed Raj and then they spoke over the phone.

'I don't believe I'm doing this,' Ankush said to Raj.

'Don't worry. Paranormal experiences are like stepping on gum, at times. You don't need to mess with them unless you have to. We, at Indian Paranormal Society, have a very scientific approach to determine the truth. We begin an investigation by trying to prove that it isn't anything supernatural. Only if we come across evidence that proves otherwise, we conclude that it's something beyond human understanding,' Raj explained.

The calm and rational explanation convinced Ankush. He was in and asked, 'How do we start?'

Raj visited Ankush and Swati's house for the first stage of IPS's professional paranormal investigation—client interview and preliminary investigation. When he was sure that there was something unnatural going on in the house, he called the team to travel from Mumbai.

∞

Raj initiated a Skype call with the IPS.

'Get on the next flight to Delhi, folks. We have a case to solve,' he told them.

Meghna, Siddharth and Rith are now based out of Mumbai while Mohan works in the navy and is available for a few months every year. Luckily, this incident happened while he was in Mumbai, which meant that this case would be a reunion of sorts for the team. The only difference would be that Gaurav would be with them in spirit, not physically.

'Long time!' Raj greeted Meghna, Rith and Mohan with a smile when they arrived at his flat. The rented Dwarka office had to be closed after Gaurav's death to minimize expenses. Siddharth, who was also there, had been in Delhi for a few months.

'Indeed! Gaurav would be happy to see us together today,

not giving up on his dream and vision of continuing the work,' Meghna said, smiling. She was the strongest of them, all more so because she knew the repercussions of a personal loss better than the others. She had lost her father a few years ago, and an incident after the tragic loss had made her determined to contact Gaurav and join his team.

Once they had all settled in, Raj explained the case to the team.

'Let's do it,' Rith said immediately, offering his hand to the team.

Siddharth put his hand on top of Rith's. Raj, Mohan, Meghna joined and cheered—cheered for each other and for the team!

'We are back!' Raj laughed, hugging them all. It had been a difficult time for all of them but for Raj, particularly, because he had been alone in Delhi after losing his best friend.

'Thank you, Meghna. You made this happen,' he told her.

Meghna observed that Raj's eyes were moist and realized that so were hers. It was an emotional period for all of them, but this moment gave immense joy because it reminded them of their passion for paranormal investigation, which still has one common thread—Rev. Gaurav Tiwari.

∽

Ankush and Swati lived in their big family home in a posh locality in Delhi. Nothing had been spooky about it, but, now, the place was haunted by a spirit that had latched on to Swati. Raj had discussed the same with Ankush and his family, telling them that he would return with his team. Raj could have arranged for a few people from Delhi, who had worked with Gaurav and him earlier, but he purposely called the team from Mumbai after the call Meghna had taken a few months ago. He wanted them to reunite and continue his best friend's dream. Maybe, Gaurav would be prouder of them if they did this, watching them from wherever he was. He was there. Raj knew. So did Meghna, Siddharth, Rith and Mohan. They felt his presence around them at times, guiding them in whatever they did, watching over them like an angel.

'Take us to Swati,' Raj told Ankush after they discussed a few things in the living room over tea.

'She is in the bedroom sleeping,' Ankush informed them.

'It's not a normal sleep, Ankush. Leave it to us. You be here with your family and don't worry. We are here now,' Raj smiled and hugged him. It was just what Ankush needed then. He and his family had been going through a lot of mental stress.

The team took out their equipment—EMF meter, EVP recorder and a video camera—for this session and went inside the bedroom. Swati was still lying on the bed, her head facing the ceiling, her eyes wide open, staring at the fan.

'Swati!' Meghna called her by her name.

No response at all. She was still as a statue.

'We have come to talk, can we?' Meghna asked, as the team went closer.

The EMF meter kept spiking higher. The presence was powerful.

Siddharth switched on the EVP recorder and asked, 'Who is Kushal?'

Swati turned her eyes towards Meghna. The entity in her spoke before Swati did. It told them how much pain it was in. But who was this? Clearly, Swati was not the only person they were communicating with.

'Do you want to talk? We will listen,' Meghna moved closer and sat at the edge of the bed to let the entity know that she would be a patient listener. Empathy for the dead is of utmost importance when dealing with them. IPS follows this philosophy in every investigation.

'They killed Kushal. They killed him in front of my eyes,' the entity growled in pain.

'We understand what you must have gone through. It's easier said than done and we can't compensate at all for whatever happened to you. But, tell us, why punish Swati?'

'Who is Swati?' the entity snarled. Swati's lips quivered.

'The woman you have possessed. The body you are in right now,' Meghna said patiently.

'I'm Vanshika, not Swati,' she looked at Meghna, her eyes doing most of the talking—the agony and anger they conveyed gave the team a hint of the wrong that she must have suffered when she was alive.

A ghost, after all, is an emotion—an emotion that may be happy, sad, angry—twisted out of shape. It wants to make its presence felt and still desires being a part of the living, physical world to undo the injustice that had happened to it when it breathed.

'Vanshika, tell us about that day,' Meghna prodded.

After an hour or so, the team met Ankush and his parents in the living room again.

'Yes. Your wife is possessed and this is not something we have concluded but you know it, hence, you approached us,' Meghna began the counselling session, another integral part of the IPS's process, which it is lauded for in the field of paranormal investigation.

'This is what we have ascertained and are sure of so far,' she continued, making eye contact with Ankush and his parents. Confidence and courage are contagious and would be much needed by the family to hear and prepare for the story Meghna was about to tell them.

∞

It was six years ago that Kushal and Vanshika were madly in love with each other. They lived in the quaint little hill station of Pahalgam, with a population of less than six thousand, where everyone knew everyone! That's how it is in small places. Their love blossomed in Delhi, where they had been studying in the same college. Their hometown acted as the common link in their nascent friendship, and, soon, they realized that they had fallen for each other. One day, early in their courtship...

'Let's get married,' Kushal proposed to Vanshika while

they were out on a date.

'We are not even working yet!' Vanshika said, holding Kushal's hands, happy about the proposal but not too sure if it was the right time.

'We can marry and not allow it to hamper our careers. Vanshika, I don't think I can live without you and I just want us to be more committed.'

'But our parents,' she said hesitantly.

Kushal and Vanshika belonged to different castes, and it is sad but true that such restrictions still exist in our country. Over the course of the next few days, Kushal travelled to Pahalgam twice and convinced both his and Vanshika's parents about their relationship or so he thought.

'They are okay with it, sweetheart. We should now go to Pahalgam and confirm the dates and everything else!' Kushal reported to Vanshika excitedly upon returning from Pahalgam.

However, their families' acceptance turned out to be a malicious plan to make Kushal bring Vanshika to Pahalgam with him. The families wanted to kill the couple and protect their honour. When they reached home, they were taken to the forest. First, Kushal was beaten up badly and hung from the branch of a tree in front of Vanshika. She was tied with a rope and made to witness her lover's death.

'This is how one sets an example!' Vanshika's paternal uncle yelled as Kushal breathed his last, his eyes protruding and legs trying to fight till his last second.

Vanshika wailed hysterically, pleading with everyone to

have mercy on them.

To make them stop, she even said, 'We will not marry!' But, the group of men were furious and adamant. They were having fun doing this—killing people who should not have broken a fundamental rule of the community.

Vanshika passed out after seeing her lover die in front of her eyes. No greater punishment could have been inflicted upon her for the crime of loving someone from a different caste. In her unconscious state, she was hanged till death from a branch of the same tree.

Vanshika's spirit either didn't want to accept that it wasn't alive anymore or was still unaware of its death. In such a state, when Ankush and Swati had strolled into the same forest and sat under the same tree where the couple had been killed, Vanshika's spirit latched on to Swati's body, thinking it existed and had a physical presence.

∞

'What...what is the solution?' Ankush asked, aghast after listening to the tragic tale.

'Don't worry. Leave it to us,' Raj smiled and hugged Ankush, who was sobbing and pleading with the team to save his wife.

Over the next few days, the IPS team exorcised Swati and cleansed the couple's house. The entity they were dealing with was emotionally challenged and intended to cause no harm to anyone. It was lost somewhere between the physical world and the other world, where spirits and demons reside—a world that runs parallel to ours.

Ankush and Swati are living happily now and were recently blessed with a baby girl. They named her Vanshika. Through this scary but important chapter in their life and their counselling sessions with IPS, the couple has started looking at life after death from a new perspective.

❧

Meghna and her mother had an early dinner together after which she watched a football match on television—France vs Germany. Meghna is a diehard fan of the sport. She had fun watching it, thanked God for the wonderful day and went to bed a little later than she normally used to.

A few minutes after she had fallen asleep, a noise woke her up. Meghna sat up on her bed and looked around. There was no one around. It was dark, and she realized that there had been a power cut.

She switched on the flashlight of her mobile phone and opened the window, as it was hot. It had been a few hours since the long shadows of the evening had dissolved into darkness. The air outside was cool, and she could hear the crickets calling.

'I'll go and check on Mom,' Meghna thought because of the noise she'd heard.

She walked towards the other bedroom, where her mother was. She passed through the living room, and the small nook, where she kept her computer. The flashlight shone through the pitch blackness and was the only source of light till Meghna noticed that her computer was switched on. But how could that be? She hadn't used it the entire day and, moreover, there was no electricity then. How could the computer be on? She directed her flashlight towards the computer, went up to it and shut it down.

'Meghna,' she heard someone say. It sounded like Gaurav!

She turned around, moving her flashlight across the room. She couldn't breathe. It felt as if the darkness was choking her. Her heart raced, and all she wanted to do was curl up into a ball and wait for someone to save her. But no one would, no one was there, except her mother who was old and sleeping. A choked cry for help forced itself up her throat, and she felt a teardrop run down her cheek.

Just then, a white apparition appeared in front of her and vanished like a coin in a magic trick—there one moment, gone the next. The lights came on the next second and Meghna heaved a sigh of relief. She sat down on the floor with a thud and ruminated on what she had just seen. She looked at the clock. It was a little past 11:00 p.m.

Her phone rang the next moment. She went back to her room before answering it.

'H–hi,' it was Siddharth. It had already been a few months since he had left for Delhi, leaving behind his home and a job in Mumbai to train under Gaurav.

Meghna was unable to speak, still dealing with the effect of the frightening incident.

'Megh—' Siddharth stammered, 'Meghna, Gaurav passed away today morning.'

'*What?!*' *Meghna said loudly in fear and shock.*

'*Yes. He was found dead in his bathroom today morning, a little past eleven,*' *Siddharth said, crying.*

Meghna was in no position to speak, unable to even ask him what had happened. Siddharth understood what she was going through.

'*I'll call you back,*' *he said and disconnected to give her time to console herself. He knew how devastating this was for all of them.*

Had Meghna felt Gaurav's presence? Had he died at 11:00 a.m. and come to bid her goodbye at 11:00 p.m.?

Meghna had heard and felt him too. Now, she would feel his absence for the rest of her life.

The world turned into a blur and so did all sounds, tastes and smells. Everything was just gone. Meghna took a breath, trying to hold back the strange feelings inside her, but she couldn't. A tear ran down her cheek, and, just like that, the floodgates opened. Her tears burst forth like a dam collapsing, spilling down her face. Her chin trembled like a small child's. She breathed heavier than she ever had before. She gasped for air that simply wasn't there. Her throat burned with a silent scream. She went to her mother and woke her up, crying—there was too much raw pain inside her to be contained.

'*Gaurav is no more,*' *she told her mother, who was completely taken aback. She tried to console Meghna, but her soothing words made no difference then. Her daughter was beyond all reason, beyond all natural methods of calming.*

Her mother called Siddharth to confirm the news.

'Yes, Aunty. It's true. He is no more,' Siddharth's voice was choked. He had a lump in his throat as he spoke, trying hard to fight back his own tears. He had been crying for hours, too.

❧

TWO

A Cursed Life

With the Kashmir case successfully closed, IPS was back after a short hiatus and it was clear that they were here to stay and live Rev. Tiwari's dream. Yes, the costs had to be minimized so the Delhi office was shut down and it was Raj who asked all team members to operate from home when they were not on their day jobs.

Even when Gaurav had been around, it had not been easy for the organization to sustain. Despite getting a lot of media visibility, when it came down to analysing the profits and losses, with every passing month, their financial burdens increased. Although Gaurav had not started IPS with a financial motive, at the end of the day, everything boils down to profits when it comes to running an organization. The team had been doing it as a passion; however, business sense and passion don't necessarily go hand in hand. The cost of renting an office and expensive equipment to reveal the factually verified truth costs a lot. The expenses had always been a lot higher than the rather paltry amount the team received from clients, and most of them only paid for travel. The team only does it because they are held together with one motive—knowing the unknown.

Soon after the Kashmir case, news spread among the paranormal investigation fraternity and others through a few media channels, and it was clear that IPS would continue its services and help people in need. A few weeks after Swati's case, Raj got another case for which he called the team, not to Delhi but Udaipur, where he had travelled first to meet the client and conduct a pre-investigation; he had been there anyway for another case that he had taken up individually. However, for this case, he knew the team would be needed. Moreover, he also wanted the team to be occupied and to keep meeting each other. Raj is still the operations and technical head of the IPS and is a reputed name in the field, who many can count on and has a huge fan following for his work. He took up this responsibility after Gaurav passed away.

∾

A family of six—husband, wife, their three daughters and the paternal grandmother, who had been put up at the family's ancestral home with other relatives—from Udaipur had enquired about the investigation process at IPS. It was a joint family but their part of the ancestral house was separated from the rest of the family. The husband—Dhananjay

Shekhawat—his wife and three daughters had moved to Jaipur for a few years, but, after a string of unsuccessful corporate stints, he decided to move back to his hometown and start a new business. During their absence, Dhananjay's mother—Sulochana Shekhawat—had lived with the rest of the joint family so that she didn't feel lonely.

Sulochana was a strong woman who had single-handedly brought up all her children after her husband's early demise. The family looked up to her, as she was the eldest among them and led by example. She even used to run the family business until a certain time when losses had started mounting up and the family decided to shut it down. She was also responsible and acknowledged for all of their good times. Sulochana's youngest son—Dhananjay—who she was closest to had moved to Jaipur but failed to earn a living there.

'Come back, son. We will arrange for some funds and you can start a small business here,' Sulochana had told him, unable to bear the struggles her darling son had gone through during the last six years. When he came back with his family, she moved back to their part of the house to live with Dhananjay's family.

However, something wasn't right. It all started from the first night of Dhananjay's family returning. Sulochana was awakened by a whistling sound, and she heard someone walking in the corridor just outside her bedroom, as if someone was dragging their feet and probably limping. It was all too clear in the silence of the night and sounds often echoed because the house was big. Sulochana got out of her bed and walked out to check who it was but didn't see anyone.

'I'm hearing things,' she told herself and went back to bed.

The next morning onwards, she started feeling a presence around her. Someone was following her everywhere, she could feel it. After a few days, the entity made it apparent as well. Sulochana would suddenly be pushed by an invisible force. One evening, she had prepared her son's favourite kaali dal and wanted to serve him with her own hands. She carried the container from the kitchen and was walking towards the dining room when someone hit her hand hard and the dal spilt all over the floor. The nights had gotten worse over the course of the last few weeks. Every day, at around 2 a.m. she would be awakened by the whistling sound and someone walking in the corridor. Sometimes, she even heard a laugh.

⌘

'Look, Dhananjay ji, it is very normal for entities or spirits, if you want to call them that, to do such things to make their presence felt. In most cases, there is always a reason behind such activities. We will need to know a little more about your family,' Raj said as the team got ready to conduct their first round of investigation. The team was to live in the Shekhawats' house for the next few days, as Raj had recorded high spikes during the pre-investigation. He had told the team that he sensed the entity was strong and wanted to communicate something. The house probably needed cleansing.

The first day didn't yield any great results. Though the presence was identified, intelligent communication was not established. In the second phase of their investigation, the entity began answering them through spikes on their EMF meter.

'If yes, one beep. If no, two!' Siddharth said, before starting the session. He repeated it thrice so that it was clear.

'Are you with us now... here?' he began.

No response.

'I repeat. Are you with us now?'

Beep!

'Are you unhappy?'

Beep!

'Is there something you want to tell us?'

Beep!

'We are all ears. You can communicate. You have all the permission to use my energy to manifest yourself.'

Silence—the kind that makes you uncomfortable.

'Show yourself!' Siddharth repeated.

Just then, the window in the room opened with a bang. The wind blew through the house powerfully, scattering old documents, as if they were the leaves of fall, and banging the doors in an almost chaotic drum beat—a marching band of one without fingers or hands.

'It's a sign,' Siddharth said, looking at everyone in the room.

Meghna started clicking as many photos as she could. She was an expert at it.

'S-U-L-O-C-H-A-N-A,' they heard a female voice. It was unhappy. It wanted to say something.

The wind stopped and everything was normal again.

Siddharth analysed the EVP recordings after this and heard the same thing repeated over and over again. The entity certainly had some connection with Sulochana.

'We need to talk to your mother, Dhananjay,' Raj said as they wrapped up for the night.

Next morning, the IPS team met Sulochana after breakfast. She had been putting up in the other area of the house with her elder son during this time, at Dhananjay's suggestion. He didn't want his mother to be affected any more since it was obvious that things had started happening to her only after moving in with them.

'Is there something you would want to tell us?' Meghna began the conversation.

'No,' Sulochana replied, looking straight into Meghna's eyes.

'We have ascertained that the entity has some connection with you; perhaps, a deceased family member who has some unfulfilled wish and wants to communicate it with you,' Rith added.

'Any idea who it could be?' Raj asked.

'No,' Sulochana's monosyllabic reply came.

'Your family is being affected due to something that transpired here... something that wasn't right,' Siddharth continued prodding. He had analysed the audio anomalies till dawn that day and had his own findings that he could back with ample proofs. In one of the communications, the entity had mentioned a name that partially sounded like 'su' and 'lo'. Then, there was one instance when he had heard the word 'badla' (revenge).

'I have no idea what you all are talking about. I have to leave now,' Sulochana stood up and proceeded towards the door, expressionless. There wasn't any fear or regret of committing a crime only she knew of.

'*Theh kateh javoriya cho?* (Where are you going?)' A woman's voice startled everyone in the room. Sulochana looked back and screamed. It was a voice she knew, but how was it possible?

Dhananjay sat on a chair, his eyes gleaming red as the entity spoke to them through him. It was high time she spoke. It was time she got justice.

'Sulochana!' she lashed out.

Sulochana ran towards the door, but an invisible force stopped her and threw her back. She fell to the floor and started crying, trembling with fear as Dhananjay's body stood up, serving a medium for Gayatri Shekhawat, Dhananjay's tai (father's elder brother's wife), who was no more.

∽

After Dhananjay left for Jaipur, Sulochana and Gayatri—both of them widows—lived in the same area of the house. While Sulochana had three sons, including Dhananjay, Gayatri didn't have any offspring. Though Gayatri was the wife of the eldest son of the family, Sulochana was older than her. Furthermore, her husband was a more successful businessman who had taken care of the family. Mostly because of these reasons, everyone entrusted Sulochana with the responsibility of the house. Gayatri agreed that this was for the better. She was much in awe of Sulochana and always sought her guidance or advice. It was only after Dhananjay left for Jaipur with his family that the two of them got to spend more time together. They became good friends over time and started sharing some family secrets too.

One extraordinary evening, the two women watched their favourite television serial, ate dinner and were sitting in the veranda, gossiping away about the days of yore.

'Gayatri, see how time flies. I really miss my husband. He passed away too soon. Such a loyal and wonderful man he was. They don't make them like him anymore!' Sulochana reminisced fondly. She recalled the good old days when she had first come to the house and how her husband made her feel comfortable. Obviously, it had been an arranged marriage and quite a royal one at that. Their love had blossomed later—love that had given them their three sons and a beautiful family.

'Wonderful, yes. But what about loyalty?' Gayatri taunted.

'Yes?' Sulochana asked, snapping out of her memories of the family she had nurtured all these years.

'I never told anyone this family secret of the Shekhawats, Sulochana. You will not like to hear it either,' Gayatri responded.

Sulochana sat up straight to listen to the unfathomable. The Shekhawats were perfect. So was her late husband. So is the family. She had given her life to maintaining their respect in the city.

'Your husband, Birendra Shekhawat, chose me to marry his elder brother.'

'We all know that.'

'What you don't know is that I'm from the Kanjar community. I'm not a Rajput.'

Sulochana looked at Gayatri in disbelief as she continued to spill the beans about Birendra Shekhawat, whom she and so many others deeply respected.

Young girls of the Kanjar community, a nomadic tribe in Rajasthan, are still pushed into sex work by their parents before they attain adulthood. Under the age-old tradition of Chaari Pratha, parents sell off their daughters for lakhs of rupees and even mortgage them for a period of time. Those who raise their voice against the custom incur the wrath of the panch, or five village elders of the community, who impose lakhs of rupees worth of fines.[*]

Birendra Shekhawat's elder brother, Narendra, was mentally unstable and girls would turn him down for marriage. So, Birendra had decided to get him married to someone who would have no option but to accept him. This

---

[*]Press Trust of India, 'In Rajasthan, Age-Old Tradition Sees Young Girls Pushed Into...', Business Standard, 8 December 2016, https://bit.ly/3SlV4UR. Accessed on 20 September 2022.

is when he had secretly bought Gayatri from her parents. Nobody would know this family secret, not even his own wife.

Gayatri had been no more than fifteen years old when she had been sold off to the Shekhawats and entered the household as Narendra's wife. But, Birendra, who had successfully closed this deal to safeguard his family needed his compensation. After all, it had been a big responsibility that he had undertaken all by himself. He had his eyes on Gayatri, too, when he had seen her for the first time. Then onwards, there had been another secret that he and his bhabhi would keep only to themselves—their physical relationship.

'You are lying,' Sulochana cut Gayatri off and stood up to leave.

'See, I knew you wouldn't like to hear the truth,' Gayatri said, much aware that her confession could have dire consequences. But, she had to vent it one day. It was not a secret for her but a burden she so wanted to get rid of that she had never been able to.

Anger, pain, sadness so intertwined that, perhaps, their names ought to be tweaked to reflect the true origins of those emotions. Sulochana screamed, it was as if her terrified soul had unleashed a demon. All she felt was anger, pure anger! The next moment, in a fit of rage, Sulochana took a sofa cushion and suffocated Gayatri to death. What was left after her last breath was silence, an uncomfortable silence that was to remain till Dhananjay and his family moved back to Udaipur. Gayatri's death was made to look normal. Yes, policemen were bribed in the process, too. Sulochana started living in the other part of the house and the jinxed place was kept locked for almost three years after conducting a ritual. Who knew Sulochana's coming back to where it all happened would have skeletons tumbling out of the closet? It wasn't that she hadn't guessed. Gayatri had often whistled and walked lazily around the corridor when when she had been alive and all the incidents that had happened had involved Sulochana. Those had been no mere hints; Gayatri had been telling Sulochana that she was there and still waiting for justice.

⌘

Dhananjay suddenly looked pale, even his lips were barely visible. Then, he took one step back and crumpled like a puppet suddenly released of its strings.

Sulochana admitted to the murder and was taken into custody by the police. Dhananjay moved to a hotel with his family for a few days while the IPS team cleansed the house, after which they conducted a two-day counselling session for them.

'Spirits intend to do no harm, Mr Shekhawat. They are simply there to tell us they exist and, that too, for a reason. Remember, they lived once, too!' Meghna smiled as they bid farewell to the family.

'Glad we could come together for this one, too!' Rith said, hugging Raj as they parted ways at Udaipur airport. He would be flying separately to Delhi.

'The family still has a curse to live with,' Siddharth told them. He had played all the EVP recordings over and over again the last night and had arrived at this conclusion.

'What?' They all looked at him flabbergasted.

'Gayatri has cursed the family. Her aversion towards the Shekhawats lived with her for years and its imprint will live on within the walls of the ancestral house. Houses have memories too—some good, some not so good, some terrible. They witness more than the human beings who live there. This one is no different. It's an old unhappy house with buried secrets.'

'But we cleansed the house,' they all said.

'Absolutely. The entity will mean no harm to the inhabitants of the house anymore. Not unless it is harmed. We aren't the only ones who are vulnerable in this world. The other beings are too—spirits are but a part of the universe we live in. They just live in a parallel dimension, right?' he concluded as they proceeded towards their respective boarding gates, hoping a new case would reunite them soon.

～

IPS was established by Rev. Gaurav Tiwari in 2009. Within a few years, it became a phenomenal success, garnering the visibility and mindshare of the country due to two factors—the excellent and genuine work they had come to be known for and media exposure. Gaurav had left no stone unturned to get the best for his team and their noble cause. Yes, it wasn't profitable and had major repercussions for Gaurav, which he mostly never shared and kept to himself. How he ran the show was something only he knew well. Sponsors did help at times. However, things seemed to have been falling apart after his untimely, shocking death, and, initially, the team had no clue how they would continue, but their passion and unity has kept them going.

Raj, who has a huge fan following, was not only Gaurav's best friend but someone who was much trusted. The way in which he technically developed the team after joining, coupled with his indomitable energy, led to Gaurav gelling really well with him. It also helped that they both lived in Delhi NCR. Raj learnt a lot from Gaurav and, like many others, considered him a mentor. In the years they spent together, Raj became a big name in the field of paranormal investigation. He knew that IPS had to continue doing the work and be known for it. A few months after this case, he arranged a talk—he in Mumbai, where Meghna and Siddharth spoke. Rith was caught up with some work, Mohan was off at sea and Raj didn't want to turn up. He wanted to see Meghna and Siddharth do the talking for a change. Both of them mostly maintained low profiles and believed in letting their work speak for itself, but Raj knew that in today's world, it's important to be visible. The talk was covered by news channels as well as radio stations, among other online media people.

'Where do you see Indian Paranormal Society in the next ten years, now that Gaurav Tiwari isn't here?' a reporter asked.

'Why do you think he isn't with us? He is here, watching

over us and guiding us at every juncture,' Meghna responded with a smile.

'Would you like to share with us about the latest investigation you conducted? We observe you all are maintaining a rather low profile these days,' another reporter asked.

Meghna and Siddharth laughed.

'Sure, sure! We are guilty and we will make up for not being everywhere of late. Trust us, we are much focussed on the work and are ensuring that we reach out to people and serve them. This happened a week ago, here in Mumbai itself, Siddharth started speaking as the cameras zoomed in to the two leading paranormal investigators of the country, whose work speaks more than their words.

~

THREE

Meeting Your Ghost

Rihon Bordoloi had moved to Mumbai from Dibrugarh in Assam two years ago for better professional prospects. His office was in Lokhandwala and he stayed in Dahisar, where the rent was pretty affordable. Hailing from a small city, it was obvious that it took him some time to get accustomed to the daily life in the city that never sleeps. It was so much more peaceful in Dibrugarh. The people there are simple with little or no ambition. They live at ease, unaware and unbothered about the various achievements of people in bigger cities. They work, earn and return home to spend quality time with their families. They have weekends that are utilized well—there are so many places to roam around in as well and they have both the time and energy for it. Recreation is not compromised at all, not to forget, malls and multiplexes have come up in a big way in smaller locations too. What they don't have there are better prospects for aspirational people who want to go that extra mile. So, Rihon moved when he was offered a good job in Mumbai.

One evening, he was boarding the Virar-bound fast local from Andheri that would stop at Dahisar. Travelling in Mumbai is a mess and it took him nothing less than forty minutes by auto from his office to the station, which was four kilometres away. Yes, even a kilometre can be a long distance in the city that always keeps moving, except, of course, when you get stuck in huge traffic jams. He had a monthly train pass, so he rushed to the platform as soon as he got down from the auto. His daily train originated at Andheri, and, if he could reach before time, there were chances he would get a seat. But, he was late that evening. He rushed down the staircase. The train stood there. But there was some problem. The platform was crowded—not that this was unusual—and there was some commotion, not the kind Mumbaikars witness daily while getting into or out of a train. This was different. There was something wrong. Rihon pushed his way to the front and came to know that a man had died by suicide just a few minutes ago by jumping in front of the train.

'These losers end their lives and then we have to bear the brunt by facing such issues in travelling. Could he not die in his home?' Rihon heard someone say.

'Such a peak time and this happens. We should take another train, however crowded it may be,' another person said.

The crowd slowly dispersed, leaving Rihon standing there, looking at the dead body of the man that lay on the railway track; his legs a few metres away from where the rest of his body was, blood splattered everywhere, his eyes wide open, as if he had been scared in the last split second before jumping in front of the train, but he must have said to himself, 'Let's do this.'

In that moment, Rihon's life took a new course... one that would be difficult for him to comprehend.

∽

Three days after this tragic incident, Siddharth received a call from a person he knew. This person connected Rihon with the IPS team. Siddharth, who had moved to Mumbai after Gaurav passed away, lived nearby. So, he first visited Rihon, who had taken a leave from his office for a few days. His girlfriend, Aisha, was with him and answered the door.

Does Rihon Bordoloi live here?' Siddharth wasn't expecting a lady to be there.

'Yes, yes. Please come in,' she looked terrified as Siddharth sauntered in.

Rihon walked up to greet him, terrified too. Not a smile on both his and Aisha's faces.

'Guys, first, relax,' Siddharth smiled and shook hands with confidence.

'It has been a frightening experience,' Rihon shuddered recalling something.

'I'm sure it must have been. But, there is always some reason behind such activities. Tell me all about it without hesitation,' Siddharth said, trying to make his job look easy, which it is not. It is very difficult, but it is important that the team makes the clients feel relaxed.

Rihon looked at Siddharth as Aisha sat beside Rihon and held his hands, trying her best to make her boyfriend feel better.

∽

After witnessing the tragedy that evening, Rihon reached his flat late and was in no mood to do anything. He took a bath because he had to, ate biscuits for dinner, switched off the lights and went to sleep.

Around 2:00 a.m., Rihon woke up with a jolt, sweating profusely.

'I must have had a nightmare,' he thought.

Though his eyes were open, he couldn't think why. His heart was pounding and his mind was empty. He strained his eyes, staring at the pitch darkness and breathed heavily till he could sit up and switch on the light.

'Water... I must drink some water,' he mumbled and walked towards the fridge in the same room.

He felt strangely dizzy while feeling a sense of nothingness, as if he was still dreaming. Rihon opened the fridge, quenched his thirst and just when he was about to move back to the bed, he stood there frozen! He was sleeping on the bed! For a few seconds, he was aware that the man on the bed was him and then, the next, he felt otherwise—his awareness began shifting from one body to the other. When he inhabited the supine body lying in bed, he'd see his duplicate bending over and shaking him.

'Get off my bed,' he said to the other body on the bed.

His mobile phone rang. His awareness shifted back to the body that stood awake and he answered.

'Hello, you didn't call,' it was Aisha.

She worked in an international BPO, and, since their timings were different, the couple would sometimes connect at odd hours over the phone, even for a few seconds. Normally, Rihon called her at around midnight before dozing off to sleep, but that night was different.

'Hello,' he responded in a daze.

'Hello, why do you sound different?' Aisha sounded curious.

'Do I?' he tried to ponder over his awareness. Was it still with him?

'All good?'

'No. No. A man died by suicide at Andheri station and I saw his body. It was... it was terrible,' he cried out loud.

'Rihon,' Aisha wanted to console him but couldn't.

The next moment, Rihon could see himself from the other body's perspective, the one on the bed stared blankly at the one standing. Fear and confusion took hold. Was he the man standing up or the man lying in bed?

The next second, Rihon woke up with a jolt again, gasping for air. The lights were switched on and the fridge in the room was open. Why would that be? Had it all been a nightmare?

Did he sleepwalk? So many questions bothered him all at once that he shouted and got out of the bed. He walked up to the fridge, looked at the open water bottle—someone had drank water from it. He put the cap of the bottle back on, placed it inside and shut the fridge door. As he trudged to the washroom, completely baffled about what had been going on, there he was again! He was in the washroom! The body Rihon's awareness was in could see him through the glass door. What on earth was going on? Unable to move for a few seconds in pure terror, he eventually made an effort and walked up to his doppelgänger, who hadn't seen him yet. With trembling hands, he tapped his shoulder but...the shoulder passed through him like it was thin air! The Rihon who was aware screamed at the top of his voice, and the next second, he woke up again with a jolt, sweating profusely. The lights were still on, but the fridge had been shut. He looked at the clock, ticking in tandem with his heart rate. It was 4:25 a.m. He knew this was no nightmare, there was more to it for sure. He called Aisha.

'Hey!' She sounded worried.

'Hi.'

'You sounded very scared. Better now?' Aisha asked.

'When did you—'

'I called at night. Don't you remember?'

'You called? No, I didn't speak to you. I remember I came home and was in no mood for anything. I slept early.'

'No, Rihon. We spoke at around 2:10 a.m. Check your call log.'

Rihon checked. Indeed, they had spoken. She had called at 2:14 a.m.

'I...I have no recollection of the call...I don't know... Something is wrong, Aish,' Rihon stammered and cried his heart out.

'Rihon, I'm coming over,' Aisha said and headed to his flat straight after office. She had been with him for the last three days, till they had contacted Siddharth through a mutual friend.

∽

This was a haunting of a different kind, and Siddharth didn't feel the need to call the team yet. He knew that this would be more of a counselling session, which he could take care of. Yes, if a cleansing was needed, he would ask Meghna and Rith to join him for the following visit. Mohan wasn't available then.

'Thanks for sharing, Rihon. Hungry? Let's order pizza?' Siddharth asked and smiled.

Both Rihon and Aisha were tremendously negative and worried. Siddharth had to make them feel a little relieved first.

Siddharth ordered pizza from his phone and then looked at them, still smiling. It helps.

'Firstly, let me inform you, there is nothing to worry about. Even if there is any problem, we are here,' his words were consoling.

'But what is this about?' Rihon asked, more scared than curious.

'There are many kinds of hauntings. We think that they are mostly about ghosts, witches, demons, but there is more to them. Please listen to me carefully,' Siddharth began his counselling session.

'Have you heard of people having out-of-body experiences?'

'No. What is that?'

'We all have done it while sleeping. Some do it a little more than others, but, mostly, all of us have out-of-body experiences. Very few are aware of them though. A person leaves their body and may observe it from a detached perspective, like a soul. It's believed that we have regular out-of-body experiences while sleeping, often hovering a few inches over our physical bodies. For example, if you have had dreams of flying, not ones on a flight but of literally flying or, say, being in the sky, you have experienced this at a subconscious level.'

'Does it have anything to do with my condition?'

'You have no condition, Rihon. You are absolutely fine! I'll come to it,' Siddharth paused before continuing.

'An out-of-body experience is a good example of an autoscopic phenomena, which can start with simply feeling the presence of something or someone next to you. Now, I'm coming to your "condition",' Siddharth laughed while making air quotes. He was trying to make the conversation as lively as he could.

Just then, the doorbell rang.

'Ah, piping hot, yummy pizza! They made it really quickly, haan?'

Siddharth, Rihon and Aisha served themselves as they continued the session.

'So, the doppelgänger effect takes this phenomenon to another level altogether. A person may hallucinate that they are actually seeing and interacting with themselves—a visual double!' Siddharth explained.

Rihon began, 'That's—'

'Unbelievable?'

'No, I didn't mean that.'

'But you nearly meant it! Let me tell you there is a very thin line between science and the paranormal, at times. In fact, there are many phenomena that both doctors and parapsychologists study, albeit differently. A good example is past life regression. In neuroscientific terms, it is called heautoscopy. It is different from other out-of-body experiences. As part of this, you may perceive an illusory body and your centre of awareness can shift from within the physical body to the illusory body and back, this can happen very frequently and very quickly! There is movement, there is sharing of emotions and sometimes of thoughts too!'

'But why does it happen?'

'There can be many reasons for it. In your case, it started with you seeing the dead body of the person who committed suicide at the station. Remember the moment you saw it. Remember the deep unsettling impact it must have had on you. True?'

'Yes. You are right. It was a sad sight, Siddharth. I stood there and stared at it for a few minutes as if I was hypnotized. But I wasn't. I was simply numb.'

'Yes, that's what happened. Then, you came back to your place, still very disturbed by the incident. It was a repercussion of the trauma. But, Rihon, there can be more to it,' Siddharth paused, took the last bite of the pizza and then continued, 'Some consider it to be an ill omen, that brings bad luck with it, more like a premonition. Interestingly, Abraham Lincoln had claimed to have seen his doppelgänger. He saw a double reflection of himself in a mirror. While one face was okay, the other was paler and looked sick. Allegedly, he shared this haunting experience with his wife too. She was worried, as it was a bad omen. Lincoln served his first full term but didn't live to finish his second. There are many such supposedly true incidents. Queen Elizabeth I was rumoured to have seen a corpse-like figure of herself lying on her bed before her death. But we, at IPS, would not like to believe in such theories. Paranormal investigation takes on a more scientific approach these days. For instance, we look at it from different dimensions and time phases, which may be operating at the same time. Simply put, there can be more than one version of you existing at the same time in alternate realities. At times, it can also be caused due to people suddenly gaining the ability to tap into another time phase to view alternate versions of themselves or other people.'

'But can trauma cause such a phenomenon? I mean, I agree it was a sight that shook me and left a deep impact, but still.'

'Yes, why not? Mental illnesses, like schizophrenia, or even brain tumours can cause people to hallucinate about versions of themselves. This is also common among people with epilepsy, especially just before they are about to have a seizure. In your case, it must have been your trauma or you have other emotional baggage.'

'I feel so relieved after talking to you. Thank you for coming, Siddharth,' Rihon got up and hugged him.

'It's my work, Rihon. I love doing it. If you want, we can cleanse this place, but if you ask me, it won't be required. It was an incident, and a terrible one at that, I agree. Try to pass it off as a nightmare and get back to your normal routine. The more you think of it, the more you will be disturbed. Don't forget, an idle mind is the devil's workshop!' Siddharth hugged him back and bid the couple goodbye.

❧

'Gaurav would have been so proud of you,' Meghna said after Siddharth updated her about the case on a call later that night.

'He is proud of all of us. I can sense it. I can sense him,' Siddharth smiled, hung up and switched off the light to catch up with some sleep. The week had been hectic, with him juggling between his passion of paranormal investigation and going for job interviews. On the other hand, Meghna had recently

relocated to a new apartment with her family. Shifting within the same city can be hectic, too, especially if you have lived in a place for many years.

A few minutes after Siddharth drifted off to sleep, a noise woke him up.

He knew that sound. He had heard it earlier too. It sounded as if someone was squeezing a plastic bottle. Yes! Yes! It was the same noise he had heard at the IPS office in Delhi when he had put up there for a few nights.

Siddharth knew what he had to do. Normal people get scared during such occurrences and either run away or try hard to ignore and go off to sleep. Paranormal investigators get up, take out their equipment and start investigating! So did Siddharth. He switched on the EMF meter and his favourite EVP recorder, which allowed him to analyse sound anomalies and started asking questions.

There was an entity present with him in the room, and the beeping on the EMF meter had already proved it.

However, intelligent communication didn't begin until a few minutes later.

'Let's wrap up soon. I have to wake up early,' Siddharth said sarcastically.

Once the session got over, he sat down to listen to the anomalies. Not much made sense till he played it on rewind...

'SAVE MEGHNA... SAVE MEGHNA... SAVE MEGHNA...' a hoarse and flat voice repeated.

Siddharth called Meghna immediately.

'All okay?' Siddharth asked worriedly, waking Meghna up.

'Yes, why?' Meghna said groggily, sitting up.
'We...We need to meet.'
'Okay, let's plan something...'
'Tomorrow!'

FOUR

The House of Secrets

Divyanshu and his wife Gini had been planning a vacation for quite some time now. They wanted it to be a rather long one and completely disconnect from the outside world while they were away. So, they decided not to opt for a hotel but a homestay, away from the madding crowds of towns, in a secluded hill station. Just the two of them and a few people they would probably not be able to avoid.

'You better keep your phone switched off,' Gini told Divyanshu while they were on the way from Salonibari airport in Tezpur to Tawang, where they were going to stay—a long journey of close to ten hours. She held his hands tightly as they moved up to the hills, taking the twisting turns on the mountainous road. Amidst the infinitely green hills, the rolling verdant hues that flowed into gold, the road stretched onward, hugging the land, taking each turn in easy stride. The winding grey road shone silver in the fresh mountain sunlight. The couple let their eyes run over each hue, seeing imperfections, yet feeling as if they were details created by an artistic hand, rendering them all the more beautiful.

Tawang, still being an uncommercialized, non-tourist location, doesn't boast of good infrastructure or roads, which can make it quite a pain to reach. However, once you get there, it is nothing short of heaven. It was already late afternoon and they knew the couple wouldn't reach on time; it would be dark soon, as is the case in most hilly places. They decided to complete the remaining journey the next morning, as suggested by their driver. They booked a homestay for the night in Dirang, which is approximately 140 kilometres away from Tawang.

They reached the homestay at around 6 p.m. and it was already dark by then. It was an old, unrenovated house, not quite the luxurious lodging experience. The receptionist, an old man from the family that owned the homestay, informed the couple that they would be transforming it into a posh little place very soon. However, for now, the area was the sanity of the hills—one where no development had occurred so far, despite some of the change happening in nearby localities. The bricks of the old house had withstood blistering summers and weathered many a hailstorms with much dignity. The blue door was worn out, having withstood the harsh weather for many years. After noting down the details of the two guests in their register, the old receptionist sat back in his wicker chair, listening to the sounds of the village and the chattering wildlife around. Their driver was from Dirang and went home for the night.

For some strange reason, Divyanshu felt very drowsy as soon as they checked into the room. His head had become foggy by the time they walked in to the corridor, as if he had been in an alcohol-induced oblivion, but he was a teetotaller. He felt as if his eyelids weighed more than they should and gravity seemed to have increased ten-fold. Everything, from his arms to his feet, felt heavy. He let his head loll from one side to the other, closing his eyes as he wallowed into the darkness. Some nightmares appear as visual puns and communicate metaphorically, offering suggestions and seeking answers in return, for what is a nightmare but a form of internal communication!

Divyanshu had the scariest and strangest dream—he and his wife were seated in the back of the jeep they had rented in Tezpur, looking straight out through the windscreen without batting their eyelids. The driver sat in his seat, immobile. The vehicle stood atop a hill. There was no sound of the engine. The vehicle simply stood there with the three of them inside.

The next moment, Divyanshu could see dead bodies all around them, all of them lying lifeless on the ground. Most of the bodies had been mangled and butchered, there was blood everywhere...all the eyes of the dead bodies were wide open, as if they had seen something terrifying and the next second, they had died.

When Divyanshu woke up, it was around 9:00 p.m. and he had no clue that he had overslept.

'We should eat,' he told Gini and called the reception to be informed that there was a small eatery a stone's throw away, which might be open, as the owner operates it from home.

They got dressed, walked while breathing the fresh chilly air, had their fill of local delicacies and retuned at 10:00 p.m. to see a little boy seated opposite their room.

'Hello! What's your name?' Divyanshu asked.

The boy didn't reply. He just sat on the floor, looking straight ahead, as if he hadn't heard Divyanshu.

'All good?' he asked again, but understood that the boy must have been disinterested in speaking with them.

'Strange boy,' Divyanshu told Gini as they walked into their room. He wanted to check on the kid again, as it was late at night. So, he peeped through the door but there was nobody! It was impossible for anyone to leave within just a few seconds, and that too, without making any noise in the empty corridor. He immediately called at the reception.

'Which boy? There isn't anyone else here except you two and me,' the old man told them.

'It could be a kid from the neighbourhood, maybe? He left without us noticing. Do you think that's possible, Divyanshu?' Gini consoled her husband, who had been going through a lot more than her lately. However, soon after, Gini had her share of strange experiences.

It was almost 1:00 a.m. and Gini hadn't been able to fall asleep. So, she decided to take a warm shower. In the shower, she felt someone pull at her mangalsutra. Gini first thought that she was imagining it. Then, it happened again! And again! And again till she let out a scream.

While this was happening to Gini, Divyanshu was fast asleep, seeing another nightmare—he could see the room numbers on the doors of the house they were putting up at. Then he opened the doors one by one and there were coffins inside—old, dark coffins, stained red, with a silver lining on each of them.

He jolted out of his nightmare, hearing his wife scream.

'We should leave! We should leave,' she came out running into the bedroom and hugged Divyanshu, still trembling with fear. Something was just not right about the house.

Divyanshu called the driver straight away, without wasting any more time.

'We will pay you more than the amount due. Just come! NOW!' he shouted.

'*Shri Guru Charan Saroj Raj...*' Gini started chanting the Hanuman Chalisa while they got ready as quickly as they could, packing their bags. They opened the door to step out.

There was an old man sitting exactly where the strange boy had been seated when they had returned from dinner. He sat still without any movement, an evil smile plastered on his face, his eyes wide open as if to complement that smile. Divyanshu and Gini cried out in fear and rushed towards the lift.

'Let's...let's take the stairs. This thing will take time!' Gini shrieked, but Divyanshu asked her to wait. The staircase was dark and dingy. It could be more dangerous and creepier for sure. Strangely, although it wasn't monsoon, they noticed that it was raining quite heavily. Then, a thunderstorm struck and it made a loud roaring noise. In the hills, it is quiet everywhere, which can make the thunder sound very fierce.

When they finally reached downstairs, the old man at the reception wasn't there.

'Hello!' they both called for him and realized they hadn't asked him his name.

No answer. Then, there was a power cut and all they could see in the darkness were the flashes of lightning accompanying the loud thunder.

'Let's just step out,' Divyanshu said. He held Gini's hand and proceeded towards the door when they heard the old man behind them.

'Did you also see the lady, apart from the man and his son?' his voice sounded different. He seemed to be mocking them.

They turned around to check, albeit reluctantly. After all, curiosity is a basic human instinct.

'Yes or no?' the man demanded as lightning struck again. The flashes illuminated the room for a few seconds, allowing the couple to catch a glimpse of the old man. He looked paler and older than he had been. They also noticed that something was wrong with his eyes.

The next second, it was dark again, but those eyes looked straight at the couple, gleaming red with sheer evil.

Divyanshu held Gini's hands tighter.

'RUN!' he shouted, and they sprinted out of the main

door. Just as they stepped out, the lights came back on. The old man sat in his wicker chair in the veranda outside.

'All good?' he asked, looking at them blankly. Nothing seemed to have happened. Everything suddenly seemed to be back to normal. The car was waiting for them in the driveway of the house.

'You were—' Gini started speaking.

'Just get into the car,' Divyanshu cut her off. There was no need to say anything. They needed to simply leave!

'Tawang?' the driver asked sleepily.

'No! Back to Tezpur. We will take the next flight out of here,' Divyanshu said.

It was almost five and a half hours' journey from Dirang to Tezpur. The couple had rushed out of the homestay at around 1:30 a.m., unaware of the road or rain. The car moved down the hills, lights on full beam. Gini watched the bright yellow light scatter through the deluge of seemingly solitary drops. The flag on the car fluttered violently in the wind, so much so that Gini wondered if it might break away from the pole.

Looking at the driver, Dongtu, Divyanshu said, 'Dongtu, can we stop for a quick bite somewhere?'

There was no answer.

'Dongtu.' Divyanshu called him again and tapped his shoulder.

'Later,' Dongtu responded gravely, not in his jovial style.

'Let it be,' Gini told Divyanshu and held his hands and put her head on his shoulder.

Divyanshu felt that something wasn't right. It was pitch

dark outside and the only source of illumination were the headlights of the car, but it felt like a never-ending road.

Divyanshu switched on his phone. The network was obviously weak but good enough for him to switch on the navigation. He typed Salonibari airport and waited for a few seconds while it buffered. The app showed the results: *3 hours and 11 minutes*. But, it didn't start navigating. Network issue. Yes, could be. So, he restarted the app and tried again. *3 hours and 30 minutes*, it read.

'This isn't possible. This isn't possible!' he yelped, sitting up and looking outside the window.

'What happened?' Gini, who had dozed off, asked. Her husband's impatient cry had woken her up.

'This place,' he pointed outside, 'we have already crossed this place before!' he cried.

'Of course, we must have crossed it on our way from Tezpur to Dirang,' Gini tried to reassure him.

'No! No, Gini, I mean now. We crossed this place close to thirty minutes ago!' he screamed in terror. Pure terror.

'You are imagining things, baby. Please tell me you are,' she was terrified and hoped what her husband had said wasn't true.

'Stop the car, Dongtu!' Divyanshu screamed.

But the driver wouldn't listen. He continued driving, his eyes straight on the road, staring at it as if he was under some hypnosis.

'Dongtu,' Divyanshu tapped at his back.

No response at all!

'STOP THE CAR!' Divyanshu and Gini screamed at the same time.

Gini looked at the rear-view mirror and saw the driver's face. Slowly, from an expressionless face, it changed to that with a smile—an evil smile. Dongtu looked at the couple through the mirror first, his eyes gleaming red, just like they had seen with the entities back in the homestay. Then, Dongtu turned around to face them, grinned and said, 'Shhh, shut up.'

This was not Dongtu! No way it could be.

Gini began chanting the Hanuman Chalisa again.

'Please let us go. Please stop the car,' Divyanshu pleaded.

But Dongtu was not in the mood for any disturbance. He drove past the hilly turns at great speed, a risk on an empty hilly road at night.

All of a sudden, the car screeched to a halt.

'What is going on?' Dongtu asked, baffled. Then, he looked back.

'All okay, Sir?' he asked, his eyes telling the couple how puzzled he was, as if he had no clue about what had been happening with him.

'Dongtu, just drive! Let's get the hell out of here,' Divyanshu shrieked while Gini continued to chant.

∞

Divyanshu had contacted the IPS team through their website a few days after he and his wife reached home in Delhi. He had been an avid follower of Gaurav Tiwari and wished the man was alive; people might as well get to watch one more investigation done by him on the television. Nevertheless, he knew Gaurav's team would do a great job of helping them.

Raj, Siddharth and Meghna decided to travel to Dirang on their own and investigate the homestay. Divyanshu had strongly recommended them to do so, as he wanted to know more about the haunting. While he didn't accompany them, he kept following up with them over the phone. It had been close to a fortnight since that frightening night, not just in the homestay but after it too, on their way down to Tezpur—an experience they would never be able to forget, a memory that they would never be able to erase.

While the team checked into the homestay, the old man at the reception looked at the three of them and smiled. Quite obviously, they would be the only guests for that night too.

Meghna was going to stay in a room alone while Raj and Siddharth were sharing another. Just like Divyanshu, Meghna started feeling extremely drowsy as soon as she entered the corridor.

'I should catch up with some sleep,' she said drowsily.

'We will freshen up and wait for you. Then, we can go out and eat something before we begin investigating at night,' Raj replied as they proceeded to their respective rooms.

Strangely, Meghna had almost the same nightmare. Despite the slight differences, what connected Meghna and

Divyanshu's nightmares were the dead bodies and the hilltop, where the car was. She woke up at around 9:00 p.m. and called Divyanshu to draw parallels.

'There is something about that hilltop,' Meghna told Raj and Siddharth, explaining whatever she could recall of her dream.

When they asked the old man at the reception about the location, he informed them that there was one close to the homestay.

'It was a burial ground in the 1960s,' he told them.

'That's where the truth is,' Meghna's eyes lit up, as she understood the significance of the dead bodies in the nightmare.

'The spirits here want to tell us something,' she told Raj and Siddharth.

'We should begin investigating,' Siddharth suggested. They skipped dinner and got straight to work. Food for soul—which, for them, was catching some ghosts—was more important than food for the stomach!

The old receptionist had given the IPS team the permission to investigate, as he wanted to prove the strange happenings in the homestay to his family members, who owned the house but lived in Malaysia. He was a distant relative who had been entrusted with the responsibility of being the caretaker of the house, which was being renovated as a homestay, in lieu of some money. He had been aware of all the strange incidents that had been transpiring at the house, but when Divyanshu called him from Delhi and told him about their experience, he knew he had to take a stand. He now wanted to share a report with the family and ask them to let him out of the contract. He could move somewhere with the money he had saved in the last three years and live the remaining years in an old age home, as he had no children. The spirits hadn't harmed him yet but the incidents had impacted him.

Meanwhile, the IPS team began their investigation in earnest. The EMF meter spiked the moment it was switched on. But, before reaching any conclusion, the team switched off all electrical appliances around, as the spike may have been caused by the devices. However, the spike persisted, indicating that there was a strong paranormal presence in the house. Meghna took her camera and began taking as many photographs as she could. Siddharth began an EVP session, trying hard to begin an intelligent communication with the entities around.

They walked in the corridor over and over again and asked various questions. Raj checked inside all the rooms, only six of them, but all he could gather was the fact that the place was haunted, spirits resided there—ones that were not at peace. They could not establish any communication with the spirits. Clearly, they were in no mood to talk.

Raj checked with the old receptionist a few months after their investigation and was informed of no reported paranormal activity.

'We will come once again to reinvestigate,' Raj told him.

'The next time you come here, you won't find me,

Mr Raj. I'm leaving in a few days,' the man informed him.

~

A few days after Meghna had moved into a new apartment with her family, Siddharth had asked her to accompany him to Rihon's place. However, understanding how tied up she had been in the midst of the relocation, he had told her that he would manage the counselling part and update her if a cleansing was required. But, the intelligent communication that he had experienced the night he returned from Rihon's house had clearly asked him to SAVE Meghna. Concerned, he had planned to meet her the very next day.

The building Meghna had moved into had been unoccupied for over two years for unknown reasons. The broker had just told her family that it had been a disputed property, but it was all sorted now. Until a few weeks ago, it had been an abandoned building, under construction for close to seven years. It had stood there for two years, like it didn't belong to the place, until a puja had been conducted.

Now, it was a co-operative housing society in the midst of the hustle bustle of big city life in Malad. Gradually, the flat owners started moving in one by one and the brokers had one more property in the locality that they could market to tenants. Real estate is a big business in Mumbai and many brokers prefer renting to buying and selling. It has its own perks and getting a tenant is always easy, as Mumbai is a city where many people from across the country and abroad move in every day.

Often, one might come across brokers who don't tell potential tenants the whole truth about a place—some of these are good, but some aren't.

This is the premise for Meghna's story—she had no clue that she would be investigating her own house very soon.

❧

FIVE

An Affair after Death

Asha Mehra lived alone in Gurugram. Her husband, Dilip Mehra, was a senior employee at an MNC based out of Dubai since three years. Although they had planned for Asha to shift to Dubai six months after Dilip went there, it never happened. Asha worked, too, and there wasn't any scope of a transfer to Dubai in her organization. She could well have left her job, relocated and tried to find a job in Dubai, but that wasn't easy, particularly since she was doing well at her current stint.

Dilip travelled to Gurugram once every six to seven months to be with his wife, but the last year had been very hectic and the couple hadn't met for a long time. They had been married for seven years now, and most of this time they had spent apart. It was an arranged marriage and though love does blossom during wedlock for many, theirs had been a more formal relationship so far. There was no one to blame for it though. Both were working professionals who didn't have much time for each other, even when Dilip was in Gurugram. The long distance between them only added to this. By the time seven years were over, Asha realized that their marriage was more of a formality for both of them. Neither of them had really worked towards making the relationship successful. They had been speaking even lesser over the phone in the last few months. It was as if even that wasn't important anymore.

Asha had contacted Raj after experiencing a string of strange incidents in the last few weeks. Raj visited her for a pre-investigation. She stayed in a high rise in one of the posh sectors of Gurugram, and there was nothing ghostly about the place, initially. Moreover, Raj had switched on his EMF meter as soon as he entered the premises and headed to the apartment in one of the blocks. No unnatural spike occurred except for those caused by the electronic gadgets around. There wasn't even any spike after he entered the apartment and Asha greeted him with a smile.

'So, how does this work?' she asked as Raj sat on the sofa.

'I'll tell you. But I need to know what's going on here.'

'I'm not too sure myself. I have these nightmares... terrible ones, really,' Asha's voice quivered with fear as she recalled and shared her experience.

She worked in a fintech startup based out of Gurugram, not very far from her house. She occupied a high-pressure managerial role, which meant long working hours. At times, she would get really late and getting an Uber or Ola from the office would become a problem, as it was a little far away from the main road. So, she would usually walk for close to five hundred metres, where she could get an auto.

On a cold night, she left the office at around 10:00 p.m. and started walking on the empty street leading to the main road. Suddenly, a strong, putrid smell met her nostrils. She looked around to see if there was any dead animal or bird nearby. It might even have been a dog hit by a car. She strained her eyes to see, as the street light was somewhat dim but found nothing. The air felt thick, like a fog, and the temperature seemed to be changing quite drastically— it kept suddenly alternating between warm and cold. Asha opened both the Ola and Uber applications on her phone and tried to search for a cab. There were none around. She began walking faster and tried calling Dilip so that she could have some company over the phone. It went unanswered, like most days.

'It must be 8:30 p.m. there, he must be back home, but he still won't answer. To hell with such marriages,' she muttered and kept walking.

'Asha,' someone whispered in her ears. She stopped in her tracks, shocked. The temperature around her got warmer in the next few seconds as if there was something around her. She could feel a presence, and it wasn't anything good. Asha looked back to check how far she had come and if she could run back to her office and lock herself inside. No, it was too late. She was somewhere in the middle of the street.

The next moment, she heard a growl coming from everywhere around her at once—it started with a low rumbling sound, which grew louder within the next few seconds, so much so that Asha had to cover her ears with her hands while running towards the main road.

Since that night, she had been experiencing strange occurrences, aside from the nightmares, which left her depressed when she woke up in the morning. She remembered some but not others. However, they all made her very sad. She always felt a strong and negative presence around her wherever she went. It followed her everywhere and she kept feeling cold one minute and hot and sweaty the next. The situation only got worse and Asha requested her reporting authority to let her work from home for a few days.

The night before she got in touch with Raj, Asha had an early dinner and decided to watch a movie in the living room. When she was in the mood for it and got time, she used to connect her laptop with the television and watch movies on one of the various OTT platforms. However, strangely, to her utter confusion, she couldn't find her laptop on the table she had kept it on before dinner. She had been working, after which she had shut it down and left the room to cook something quickly. Asha was sure about this. Where could it be? She frantically searched for it everywhere in the apartment. After an hour or so, she returned to the room and found it on the table, exactly where she had left it.

'The phenomenon of objects disappearing is known as apportion and that of objects reappearing is called asportion. They are both fairly common phenomena,' Raj stated after he listened to Asha patiently.

Raj contacted the IPS team in Mumbai the same evening. Siddharth flew down to Delhi the next morning. Meghna, Rith and Mohan couldn't make it, as they were tied up with other commitments and this case was too short notice. Raj picked Siddharth up from the airport, they roamed around Connaught Place, had a sumptuous meal at Berco's and headed for Gurugram. Though Asha had been working from home, obviously, they would begin the investigation in the late evening. The logic behind this being: there is less interference when it's dark although ghosts are very much active during the day too. Raj and Siddharth spent some more time in DLF Cyber Hub, catching up on all current news, before reaching Asha's apartment. Nonetheless, they were much before time.

'Have any other incidents occurred since last evening?' Raj asked after greeting Asha at the door and introducing Siddharth.

'No, Raj. But I can feel the presence around me all the time. I didn't have a nightmare last night though,' Asha watched as the two of them unpacked their bags and took out their equipment.

'Ghosts and spirits are active all the time. Most of the times, a haunting has a purpose. We need to find that to understand its intent,' Siddharth said and enquired about the hotspots i.e., places where most of the paranormal activities had happened.

'This is a little different if you ask me, Siddharth. I told you I barely found any spike on my EMF meter yesterday.

The presence here is in no mood to communicate, it seems,' Raj told him and began taking random photographs on his full-spectrum camera, including some with the lights switched off.

'Let's switch off all the electronic equipment in the apartment—our phones too,' Raj told Asha and switched on his K-II meter.

Siddharth and Raj began inspecting every nook and cranny of the place, but there was just no trace of anything. After an hour or so, Raj and Siddharth sat down with Asha to further discuss the case.

'Asha, are you sure you had those experiences?' Raj asked.

'Yes, why would I lie?'

'We are not saying that. Please don't misconstrue our words. But, please understand that we have found nothing here so far.'

'Let's keep trying,' Siddharth added. He is a man of few words.

Finally, around 2:45 a.m., they got their first evidence— Raj's K-II meter beeped once, twice and then, it stopped.

'Anyone here?' they asked together, taking as many photographs as possible. Siddharth switched on his EVP recorder.

'Anyone here?' they asked again, louder this time.

The meter beeped again.

'Do you want to communicate with us?' Raj asked.

No answer. The entity was not interested in talking.

'Who are you and what do you want?' Siddharth asked

and made sure the EVP was switched on.

They asked a few more questions, after which Siddharth sat in the living room to analyse the audio anomalies while Raj continued to inspect the place all over again.

After an hour, Raj and Siddharth called Asha in to discuss their findings.

'Can we make some coffee first? We all are sleepy and it will help us stay awake,' Raj asked.

'Yes! I'm so sorry I didn't ask you,' Asha stood up to proceed to the open kitchen near the living room.

'No formalities, please! I'll make some coffee for all of us. You simply calm down and listen to Siddharth with an open mind,' Raj told her and stood up.

'Asha, we want you to be very honest with us. Goes without saying, nothing that we talk about now will go out of this door from our end,' Siddharth said, smiling reassuringly, trying to make her comfortable.

'Y—yes, I will,' Asha was hesitant but curious.

'This was a difficult haunting to crack, I'll tell you why. The entity here is in no mood to communicate.'

'I see.'

'Who is Hardik?' Siddharth asked suddenly, catching Asha unaware.

Her expression changed from curiosity to confusion to realization to acceptance all at once as Siddharth looked at her closely. He knew he had gotten it right. He just needed to know what happened.

Returning from the kitchen with three piping hot cups

of coffee, Raj offered Asha her cup of awakening, 'Coffee.'

⁂

Some office flings may last for just a few days or weeks, especially when there isn't any commitment involved from one or both of the partners. Asha was alone and lonely in the absence of her husband and, perhaps, even when he was in India. She knew that theirs was an unhappy marriage and there was no love between them, something she would have to live with for the rest of her life. But she never considered separating from him. Divorces were a complete taboo in her family and she didn't even discuss her marital problems with her parents, who lived in Bhopal.

All she did everyday was overwork, reach home late to catch up on some sleep, reach office early in the morning and overwork again. She thought she would be okay if she kept herself occupied. She was wrong.

Hardik Lamba joined the startup as a management trainee. This was his first stint as a postgraduate. He was younger than Asha, which never became an issue when it came to matters of the heart. Hardik was energetic, outgoing and jolly—everything that reminded Asha of her fun college days. Now, she missed having fun and sometimes couldn't recognize herself. She knew people change as they grow old, especially after marriage, but was it really important to? Even if it was, her life was boring and she needed a break, which she found in Hardik. They struck a chord within just a few hours and ended up spending most of their time together in office, as Hardik was assigned to Asha's team. She was to be his 'buddy'—a term used by the organization for someone who guides a new joinee in the first few weeks of his or her tenure. Asha and Hardik would sit together in her cubicle, have lunch together, grab a cup of tea in the evening while he would smoke and she would look at him, admiring his chocolate boy looks. They would talk constantly, laugh at their own jokes and steal glances at each other sometimes and smile. Very soon, Asha found herself going out with him after office hours and even on the weekends. They would sometimes catch a movie, eat out at a restaurant and visit a park, holding hands and talking. She discussed everything with him and he listened, looking at her patiently and lovingly.

Then, one day, they crossed the line. It began with a kiss—simple and sweet—steeped in passion that ignited Asha. It brought a promise of realness, of the primal desire that lives in all of us. Soon, they were in a physical relationship. Hardik would spend many weekends at Asha's apartment and they would talk, make love, cuddle and, perhaps, watch a nice movie while hugging each other under the covers. This continued for close to two months and then, Hardik proposed. He told Asha how deeply he had fallen in love with her and wanted to spend his life with her. Nothing mattered for him, not even the fact that she was married. He loved her with all his heart.

This was when Asha realized what she had always known in a way—their relationship was destined to be short-lived.

She had always been aware of the fact that she wouldn't leave Dilip since her family would never approve of it and neither would society. Initially, she had been happy and had enjoyed all the attention, love, warmth and good sex, but the proposal had left her in a daze. Her heart was elated, but her mind told her to control her emotions and be practical. The relationship had no future. She had known this but had been going with the flow until she understood that it would be too late if she continued the fling.

A few days later, Asha broke up with Hardik. He tried his best to get back with her, but she was adamant. All the office colleagues knew about the affair, which had gone awry by then. It was fodder for great gossip in the office until Hardik left the organization. Asha didn't even meet him on his last day. It did hurt her a little to avoid him, but she knew her sheer presence would ignite the restrained emotions between them.

∽

Siddharth's communication via his EVP recorder mostly yields good results when the entity wants to talk. This one hadn't been in the mood during their investigation, but Raj and Siddharth had left no stone unturned to communicate with it. Once some intelligent communication had been established, they had noticed a message that Siddharth had to understand. Among the few audio anomalies that Siddharth had analysed in the short time, he identified some key words, like 'Hardik', 'dead' and 'suicide'. This made it clear to them that the presence wasn't harmful. It had only latched on to Asha because of his unfulfilled wish of not getting to be with her in life. Gaurav's theory was right—empathy for the dead is of utmost importance, as they, too, had been alive once.

'Any idea where Hardik went? Where he is now?' Siddharth asked Asha, after a pause, having listened to Asha's story.

'No. I never kept in touch and we didn't have any mutual friends. I'm not on social media,' Asha responded.

'His contact number? You must have it.'

'Never called him or even made an effort. Yes, he did try to call me a few weeks ago. I didn't answer.'

'We are afraid he is no more,' Siddharth informed her. Asha sat up straight, unsure how to react.

'Yes. You may call his number in the morning to check, but I'm sure of our findings. Hardik's presence has been latching on to you since, what we guess, was his suicide.'

'What?' Asha stood up, not quite believing it. She knew Hardik had been a very emotional person, but could he end his life because of a failed relationship?

In the morning, Asha called Hardik's number. His father answered and informed her that his son had died in a car accident a few weeks ago.

'What's your name, madam?' he asked, unable to control his tears, recalling the huge loss. Unfortunate are the parents who have to witness their child's death.

'Asha,' she responded, feeling as if a part of her had died

after hearing the news—that part of her heart, which had feelings for Hardik, but she had chosen her mind over it. She kept regretting this choice in life.

'Asha...I know your name. Hardik succumbed to his injuries after he was brought to the hospital. He asked me to call you once so that you could come.'

Both Hardik's father and Asha broke into tears, grieving the person who connected them.

'Spirits are not always bad, Asha. We believe Hardik loved you a lot and, perhaps, he was here to tell you that he is no more,' Raj said as he and Siddharth took her leave.

❧

The co-operative housing society Meghna and her family had moved in to a seven-storeyed building with one apartment on each floor. Meghna had been tied up for a few days during the hectic relocation. She was to meet Siddharth but hadn't found the time. Then, Siddharth had travelled to Gurugram to investigate Asha's case with Raj. The first incident at Meghna's new home had happened during this time.

Meghna's brother, Gautam, had recently shifted to Mumbai from Moradabad. He was pursuing his postgraduation in Mumbai and putting up with his sister for a while. One night, he was studying in the living room when he heard a noise. Gautam looked around and saw no one there.

He heard the sound again after a few minutes. He strained to hear it clearly. It sounded like a group of people chatting with each other, there were glasses clinking, a lady's voice could also be heard—the conversations were not clear, but Gautam could make out that there was a party in progress, and it was happening right there... in the living room where he was sitting alone!

'This is unreal,' Gautam said to himself, standing up. Just then, the noises stopped as if there were people around who heard him. The next second, they recommenced. A shiver ran down Gautam's spine as he proceeded towards his bedroom. This might as well be his imagination. He had no clue. Only Meghna could help him. He decided to talk to her the next day.

Just then, he heard a woman giggle behind him. Sweat trickled down Gautam's forehead as he gathered all his courage and turned around to check who it was. He saw the woman vanish into thin air that very second! He heard her giggle again, and there she was! Standing still near the window. Gautam trembled with fear as he looked at the woman dressed in a white gown with a big red rose on it. Or was it blood? Gautam couldn't be sure. The lights had dimmed since she appeared in the house, which was obviously haunted.

'Wha—what do you want?' Gautam managed to ask loudly despite his fear.

The lady continued to giggle, her face hidden under a veil. Gautam could hear the clinking of glasses and the conversation of people having a party again.

The lady began walking from the window to the main door, almost floating while Gautam stood there staring at her, almost hypnotized. She reached the main door and disappeared again.

Then, everything fell silent. The lights were not dim anymore. Everything felt normal again. All this while, the air around Gautam had felt heavy.

The first thing next morning, he discussed the incident with Meghna. It was too early for his sister to comment anything, as she hadn't sensed anything until then, but it was clear that this had not been a nightmare.

The very next night, Gautam had another experience. Around 2 a.m., he woke up and realized that he was thirsty, walked to the fridge in the kitchen near the balcony. In the midst of the absolute silence, he heard the noises of people chatting, glasses clinking and, perhaps, someone playing a violin again. Despite being scared, he walked to the living room again. It was dark, and, barring a shaft of light from his bedroom which illuminated the area, the visibility was low.

Crack!

He heard a glass break in the kitchen. Gautam walked back to check. The fridge was still open, the light inside illuminated the space around. He strained his eyes a little—there was no broken glass anywhere. But, he was sure he had heard it.

'I'm tired of this life!' a man's frustrated and furious voice shook Gautam. He moved out of the kitchen at great speed.

'I'm tired,' Gautam heard the voice repeat. It was accompanied with a cry of sadness, of failure, of giving up.

Then, Gautam saw a man, if you could call it that. It wasn't his whole body...just a man's head in the balcony near the kitchen.

'I'm tired,' the severed head cried again.

Gautam looked at the severed head's eyes—white, dead, sad. He felt like they were telling him and his family something that they had to find out before it was too late.

SIX

The Killer from the Past

Bipin Maity returned home from tuition early one evening. A young lad of sixteen, he went to a government school near his home in Bagbazar, a neighbourhood in North Kolkata. Bipin's father, a government clerk in one of the corporate offices of a bank in the Dalhousie area of Kolkata, usually returned by 7:15 p.m., taking the metro from Esplanade to Shobhabazar. Bipin's father's wife—yes, she was his father's wife, not his mother; at least he could never call her that—would reach home around the same time. She worked at a nearby food takeaway counter, which also delivered homely food to those who couldn't cook.

Bipin's father had married twice. Bipin was the second wife's son. However, a few years after their marriage, Bipin's parents had split and his father had gone back to his first wife, taking Bipin with him. Just like that. Bipin had not even been asked what he had wanted. He had been too young to understand much of what had been going on—the abusive relationship, the hurt and pain his mother went through or the separation—but he had cried a lot over whatever he remembered. After all these years, he still hadn't moved on. The incident had deeply scarred his psyche. To make things worse, his father and stepmother never let him forget who he was. Every day, he was reminded of it. When he had been younger, both of them used to beat him. The lady of the house never accepted Bipin, but, sadly, Bipin's mother didn't have the means to nurture him.

'Let the idiot stay. We will see what we can do with him later,' his father's wife had told his father. Bipin had been sitting in one corner of the room, not understanding what was happening to him.

Over the course of the next few years, he had been ill-treated almost every day, and his father had done nothing about it. The prodigal husband had returned to his first wife, regretting everything he had done and had been living like her puppet since then. Once, Bipin had gathered some courage and spoken to his father about his issues. His father had given him one tight slap.

'You filth! You should be grateful we have not abandoned you!' His father had screamed and shut him in his room for two days without any food.

Bipin had been much embarrassed even at school. The years of pain and torture, physically and mentally had affected him very deeply. He could never be a normal kid. He rarely made friends. In the government school, which was a stone's throw away from where he lived, everyone knew about him and his family. The students laughed, they mocked, some of them abused and others thrashed him just for fun. When the cold logical part of the brain held his inner child captive in its own house of horrors, a psychopath was born, indifferent to the self and others. His empathy shut off completely and only the sick forms of joy afforded by cruelty and vice remained available to him.

Bipin greeted his elder brother, who was watching cricket on the television, as he entered the house, which would never be his home.

'You are back early,' the son of the house said.

'Yes. I have work,' Bipin nodded and went straight to his room.

A few minutes later, his stepbrother could hear voices coming from Bipin's room. 'Who the hell is he talking to? Is there anyone else here?' he pondered and decided to check it out himself.

'Bipin,' he called, opening the door of the room.

'Surprise!' Bipin cried, smiling. His eyes gleamed with manic satisfaction as he held his stepbrother by his collar and stabbed him with a long, sharp double-edged dagger. Bipin stabbed him once in his stomach, till he could feel the joy of hurting the son of the house. Then, Bipin stabbed his stepbrother again and again and again. Finally, he slit his stepbrother's throat. Blood gushed everywhere on the floor. He repeatedly kicked the corpse as hard as he could.

'You were the fucking filth! Not me!' He screamed

and cried, smashing his dead stepbrother's face until it was disfigured.

As he finished off this heinous act, Bipin realized he was hungry. He washed his bloody hands in the washroom and then, ate a few sweets from the refrigerator.

'Damn. I always told that bitch the sweets from the local shop suck. But no, she wouldn't still get me the *shondesh* from N.C. Das,' he ate whatever he could, gulped down some water. Then, he watched television, waiting for his so-called father and his wife to return.

After a few minutes, the doorbell rang.

'Ah, my dear mother is here!' Bipin jumped with joy, opening the door with a straight face.

'You are early. Why?' she demanded while walking in as if it was a crime for Bipin to come home without her permission.

'I wanted to give you a gift you deserve, you sick mind,' Bipin said calmly before tackling her to the ground and thrusting the dagger into her forehead. He pressed it in harder and pulled it out in one go; blood gushed out from the deep cut as Bipin watched his father's wife breathing her last, her eyes full of the horror and shock of the last few seconds of her life.

'Now, let's wait for daddy dearest,' Bipin said, laughing as he slit her throat, smashed her face as many times as he could, spat at it, stabbed repeatedly and laughed again.

Then, the doorbell rang again.

∽

An ardent IPS follower from Kolkata had gotten in touch with the team through their website and Facebook page. Raj had been in Ranchi for some work when this had happened. So, Meghna, Siddharth, Rith and Mohan gathered at Mumbai airport and flew down to the City of Joy to meet the person who had a case for them. Ideally, a pre-investigation happens before determining if detailed work needs to be undertaken on a case. However, their team member from Kolkata hadn't been available for the pre-investigation, and, based on the urgency that the person reporting the case had emphasized, the team decided to take it up. The person who had reported the case received them at the airport.

'Debashish,' he greeted the team and shook hands with everyone.

After exchanging pleasantries, he escorted them to his car.

'Which part of Kolkata are we going to?' Meghna asked him.

'Bagbazar,' he responded. He was a man of few words.

They got down on the main road, and Debashish led them through a maze of old houses in a part of Kolkata with minimal new construction.

They stopped at an old building, one of the many in the locality. There was nothing uncommon about it in an area that didn't feel like it was part of a city, termed as a *para* in Bengali, i.e., 'neighbourhood'.

Debashish rang the bell and an old man in a vest opened

the door. He had possibly just woken up from an afternoon nap, something many Bengalis thoroughly relish after a good meal.

'*Jethu* (father's elder brother), they are here,' Debashish told him.

'*Aashun, aashun* (please come in),' the man said, inviting them in. They all greeted each other and exchanged smiles.

It had been fifteen years since Bipin, a minor then, had slaughtered his family. Jatin Bagchi, a distant relative of the family, had moved into the house after the incident, acting as its caretaker. Months and years had passed. Jatin continued to live in the house that had witnessed the cold-blooded murders. There had been a lot of rumours about the family to start with, which further intensified after the tragedy of 2002. Rumours related to things in explicable and supernatural spread like wildfire. Over the course of the years, it was sure that there was more to these rumours. The paranormal activities had not been too explicit, but there had been many strange occurrences. Jatin lived with his wife, Uma, who had most of the stories to share.

∾

Uma had her first experience in 2008. Jatin was out for his daily evening *adda*, and she was cooking dinner. She heard someone humming from the drawing room and went to check but found nobody there. When she told Jatin about it, he laughed it off.

A few weeks later, a loud knock on the door startled Uma out of her sleep at night. Jatin, being a heavy sleeper, didn't hear it.

The knocks continued. Uma wondered, *why wouldn't the person ring the bell? Besides, it was 1:00 a.m.! Who could it be?*

She walked up to the door and looked out of the peephole, but didn't see anyone outside. Just as she thought that she might have heard things and was about to leave, someone began banging the door. She screamed and ran to wake her husband, but, by then, the banging had stopped.

'We should take this seriously!' she cried to Jatin.

A helpless Jatin, who was in two minds, called an *ojha* (an exorcist who uses religious practices to drive out ghosts), and a day-long ritual was performed. Things were back to normal after that and no activity was reported for at least a few years.

Then, one day, like every other evening, Jatin got down from a bus on the main road and was walking to his house when a young boy approached him.

'Dada, I'm lost. Could you guide me?' he asked.

The teen had curly hair, his eyes had a lost look as if he had just awoken from a nap.

'What is the address?' Jatin asked, observing the boy more closely. Something about him was familiar, and Jatin thought he had seen him somewhere.

'It's near a local sweet shop,' the boy responded.

'There are quite a few of them here. Come,' Jatin started walking and the boy followed him on the dark and empty lanes winding through the old houses.

'Are you here for a holiday?' Jatin enquired.

'No. I live here.'

'Strange, I've never seen you. Did you shift here recently?'

'No, I've been here since I was a child.'

Jatin stopped and looked at him again. How could he not have seen this boy? It was a para after all. People knew each other in such neighbourhoods.

'*Kon baarir chele?* (What's your surname?)' Jatin asked, knowing that he could easily help the boy if he knew his surname.

'Maity.'

'Okay, there are two of them here but neither are near a sweet shop.'

'It is near Babloo's sweet shop. They make terrible sweets,' the boy told him.

Jatin thought for a moment while looking at the boy.

'But Babloo's shop shut down a few years ago. And yes, there was one Maity family who lived near it. That is where I reside now. What's your name?' Jatin asked, staring at him and realizing that he had had seen the boy years ago in photographs.

'Bipin,' the boy responded before vanishing into thin air, leaving a terrified Jatin running to his house.

Jatin pressed the doorbell urgently and knocked till his wife let him in. He heard someone humming outside the door as if they were taking a stroll.

The incidents that occurred after this one were infrequent,

but, when they did occur, it was obvious that something was wrong. Jatin saw Bipin at least five more times, once in broad daylight.

∾

Meghna, Siddharth, Rith and Mohan had been listening to Jatin patiently and by the time he was done telling them about the experiences, it was late evening. The team unpacked their equipment and instructed Jatin and his wife to stay together in the drawing room.

'There is nothing to worry. We are here for you,' Meghna smiled.

The EMF meter beeped the moment she switched it on.

'This is going to be interactive, it seems,' Rith told the others as they began their work.

'Why would these incidents occur over the course of so many years? I don't quite understand,' Uma was curious.

'The dead lose their sense of time in the other world, which runs parallel to ours. In fact, time. It moves differently there, not bound by the human concepts—years, days and months have no bearing in the afterlife. But, it's believed that a minute spent in our world is equivalent to many more there. Time, if anything like it exists in the other world, moves very slowly there. The entities stuck in that realm can appear in different timeframes,' Mohan answered.

Siddharth turned on his EVF recorder and started asking questions. Meghna took as many photographs as she could.

Rith and Mohan helped inspect every nook and cranny of the house. They walked around the entire house with the EMF meter, trying to get a base reading to check if there were any unexplained EMF spikes.

'What had happened the night of 2002?' Siddharth asked several times during his session. He knew the best way to get to the crux of every case was to understand the origin.

'Jatin, there is something in this house to which the entity could still be attached? We have come across this phenomena in many such cases. Check if there is anything here, anything that has been here for a long time since before you moved in. Try to recall, please,' Meghna could sense it using her clairalience—the ability to acquire psychic knowledge through smell. Meghna felt the most extreme sensations among the team members and was, at times, affected after a few cases too. One of their cases had required her to go for a cleansing, on Gaurav's suggestion.

Uma knew where this was going and she knew where they could check—the storeroom. It was located in a corner of the house that was mostly kept locked except for one day every two to three months when Uma got it cleaned. They didn't keep their things there since most of the Maitys' belongings had been dumped there after the murders.

The IPS team followed Uma and Jatin as they unlocked the dusty and damp storeroom.

༄

The doorbell rang and Bipin went to open it again with a straight face. There was blood almost everywhere on the floor by the time he was done with his father's wife and son. Bipin just had to make sure that his father stepped in. He could obviously not have imagined his son had so much potential!

'Murder is an art,' he smiled and told himself. Bipin clearly enjoyed the bloodbath.

'Hello, Baba,' he said, letting his father in.

His father walked in, clueless of the horror his son had wreaked in the house, which was not a home for anyone anymore.

'Is your mother back?' he asked, looking around, not having noticed the bloodstains on the floor until then.

'That lady is not my mother,' Bipin yelled and attacked his father, who was in for a shock.

Bipin's knife pierced through his right shoulder, and he screamed with pain while his son shut his mouth with one hand.

'It won't hurt much. I promise, Baba. It will surely not hurt as much as you all have hurt me,' Bipin cried, tears rolling down his cheeks. He began strangling his father.

'Bi—' his father choked, eyes protruding, hands trying hard to catch hold of anything around.

'Die! Die, you scoundrel!' Bipin screamed, not letting his father breathe for a single second. He was having mixed feelings about seeing his father die in front of his eyes.

'Damn! It's not as much fun as I thought it would be!' he kept exclaiming, realizing that he still had feelings for the man. After all, he was Bipin's father. Then, all the bad memories reappeared before him, like a terrible vision. His real mother, who had pleaded with the man to not leave her, the abuses, the beating, the insults, everything that had made him the psychopath he was now.

'DIE!' Bipin yelled, letting go of his father's neck for a few seconds while holding the dagger hard to slash his neck.

Bipin's father used all his strength and pushed him as hard as he could. A tussle followed and he banged his son's head into the wall.

'Bastard!' he yelled, banging Bipin's head repeatedly against the floor till he was sure that Bipin had died. But, his son had one last breath left in him and, in that moment, he slit his father's throat, laughing one last time and thought, *what a blood bath the evening had been! So satisfying!*

Blood gushed with sickening determination from Bipin's father's neck, as if his own heart sought to pump it out of his body. He clamped his fingers over the wound, thinking it would be of some help, the deep cut grew paler by the second. The scarlet blood washed over the place, painting the scene in which the family would be found dead the next morning.

∽

'This house has seen a lot, Jatin. The anger, the hate, the negativity—all this death has birthed certain inexplicable activities. The house needs cleansing, but, for that, we need to find all the things that were here even before you occupied it,' Siddharth explained to Jatin and Uma as the others began searching the storeroom.

'We think it isn't just Bipin's spirit that is haunting the house, but all his other family members too—his father, stepmother and stepbrother. You have seen Bipin's spirit only outside this house. Your wife has heard knocks on the door, someone banging on it as if they want to desperately enter,' Siddharth paused, seeing a smile on Meghna's face. She had found something.

It was Bipin's secret notebook. During his lonely and disturbed life, he had found solace in writing about his immensely negative feelings, the emotional turbulence of his life and his thoughts. Soon, they found some other belongings of the father, stepmother and stepbrother too.

'Burn them all,' Meghna instructed.

The team spent the next two days cleansing the house till they were sure that the entities around would not show their presence or harm Jatin and Uma Bagchi.

'Remember, their world runs parallel to ours. Most of the time, we don't see or feel them, but that doesn't mean they don't exist. At times, the lines blur and they connect with our world in various ways, wanting to let their presence be known to us. There is always a reason behind this. In your case, this had a lot to do with their belongings in the storeroom, which they were attached to when they were alive. We also believe the entities here were stuck in an action. While Bipin's spirit wanted to come into the house, his father, stepmother and stepbrother wouldn't allow him,' Siddharth concluded the counselling session over cups of tea and fish fingers.

'Thank you so much, all of you,' Jatin folded his hands in sincere gratitude as the team stood up. They had a flight to catch in two hours.

'*Ki bolchen, Jatin da. Aapni aamaader theke onek boro* (don't mention it, Jatin da. You are much elder than us),' Raj responded with a smile. He was good at picking up languages and had been learning Bengali words during the last few days.

Jatin and Uma laughed, their eyes moist. They were going to miss the IPS team, not only because they helped them but also because they were fantastic, empathetic and warm people.

❧

A loud scream woke Meghna, her mother and Gautam that night. It came from Meghna's sister's room. Ekta was too horrified and had no clue how she should react when they all came running to check on her and her six-year-old daughter.

Ekta had seen the same disembodied head of a man floating mid-air that Gautam had seen some time back. All of a sudden, something had woken her up, and, right in front of her, she saw the white, sad, dead eyes staring at her.

'Aunty,' someone called her from behind. Ekta turned around to see a little boy standing at the edge of the bed, also staring at her. His eyes were sad, too, as if they had witnessed some big tragedy.

Ekta sat there looking back at him, unable to move, perhaps the fear had paralysed her or perhaps she had been hypnotized.

'Aunty, you should help us,' The boy said in a feeble voice, 'will you?'

'Will you?' he repeated.

Ekta trembled, still unable to move or utter a word.

'WILL YOU?' he roared, the sadness in his eyes now accompanied with immense anger.

SEVEN

The Secret of Empire Tower

Yuthika and Arvind were working professionals in the BPO sector for many years. Both of them had started their careers as telecalling executives in the same company in 2002. They were colleagues first; then, they became friends; and, soon, they found themselves studying in the same college on scholarships from their company. Over the course of sixteen years, they had grown by leaps and bounds. After their marriage, both of them also did stints abroad, during which they had been away from each other for two years. They had returned to Bengaluru a few months back and had decided to settled down in their favourite city. Soon after, they had bought a 3 BHK apartment and shifted into the society a month and half ago.

Empire Tower is one of the oldest high-rise residential buildings in Bengaluru. The couple were adamant about living in the central part of the city, not even some nearby suburb where property rates were a little lower. Since the property wasn't new and not as well-maintained as many others in the area, they got quite a good deal through a known source. They were happy that they could finally call a place their own after so many years of staying on rent in India and abroad. But fate had other plans for them.

It all began on the third night after they moved in. They had unpacked most of the boxes by then and had begun settling down. Yuthika was going to utilize the upcoming extended weekend to settle things; the basics had been done with the help of the office mover and Arvind had helped, too, as he returned from office earlier. The couple had different work shifts; while Arvind returned at 8:00 p.m., Yuthika usually wasn't home before 1:00 a.m. Usually, Arvind waited for Yuthika till she returned so that they could spend some time together.

Yuthika had an extra key to the apartment, because Arvind would sometimes fall asleep before she returned. That night, she opened the door, walked in slowly and switched on the light in the living room. From what she could make out, Arvind had dozed off—all the lights were switched off and there was pin drop silence. She just needed to take a bath and slip into the blanket with her husband, as she had eaten dinner in the office. So, she tiptoed into their bedroom, making as little noise as she could.

Just when she switched on the light, she saw her husband seated on the bed, staring at one corner of the room.

'Arvind! Damn! You scared me!' Yuthika screamed,

taking a second to breathe.

Arvind didn't move and didn't even bat an eyelid.

'Arvind? All good?' Yuthika asked again, walking up to her husband and staring at his face. He looked as if he was under some spell or maybe he was still dreaming. He might have been sleepwalking the very next moment had Yuthika not come in.

'Arvind!' she shook him.

Arvind looked at her, his eyes still blank.

'Who are you?' he asked calmly.

The next second, Arvind passed out. When he regained consciousness after a few minutes, he was normal again.

'I have no clue what you are talking about, Yuthika. The last thing I remember is I was feeling sleepy while waiting for you. That's it!' he told her when she probed into the matter.

Nothing like this had ever happened with them before. Neither had Arvind ever sleepwalked earlier nor did he have any other sleep-related or psychological issues. Could it be that the work pressure had gotten to him? Arvind took a leave for the next few days and decided to take some rest. This turned out to be a mistake.

During his leave, one evening, he was watching a cricket match on the television, when he was startled by a noise in the kitchen. He went and checked, but he didn't see anything. So, he resumed watching the match. After a few minutes, he heard the noise again from the kitchen. It was the sound of clinking utensils, as if there was someone there, cooking something.

Terrified, Arvind went and sat near the home temple and began praying. He knew calling Yuthika was futile, as she was in the midst of her shift. Even if she would leave office early, it would take her an hour to reach him. Also, he didn't want to show her how scared he was and that he could manage without her.

The doorbell rang.

Is she back early today? Arvind wondered, walking towards the main door. He looked through the peephole.

It was Yuthika.

'Thank God!' Arvind exclaimed in relief and opened the door.

There was nobody there!

'What on earth!' he cried.

'Looking for me, baby?' he heard Yuthika's voice from inside the apartment.

The door shut behind him. Arvind tried to open it, but it wouldn't budge. He banged and kicked it hard. His face soon turned pale when he realized what he was experiencing.

He could hear the utensils clinking again and Yuthika's voice came from kitchen.

'Arvind!'

A chill ran down Arvind's spine as he tried to remain calm while walking to the kitchen. His mind told him not to inspect it, but he was oddly curious as well. Perhaps, he had been hearing and seeing things? Was he hallucinating? At that moment, only he could distinguish between reality and illusion, or so he thought. As he reached the kitchen, he peeped in to see if everything was fine. It was. He heaved a sigh of relief and turned around to leave, when he heard a noise. What met Arvind's eyes left him shell-shocked! Utensils began dropping on the floor one by one from the racks. The fridge opened by itself.

'Arvind,' someone whispered in his ears and giggled.

Petrified, Arvind ran to the main door as fast as he could, but it was still shut and wouldn't open.

Yuthika returned home at 12:45 a.m. and found her husband lying unconscious on the floor near the main door. She contacted Raj the very next day and, luckily, he was not too far away from Bengaluru.

∽

Raj was in Mysuru for some work when he received an e-mail from a certain Mrs Yuthika Prasad, who lived in Bengaluru. He decided to postpone his return journey to Delhi and travel to Bengaluru first. He reached the given address by late afternoon and was greeted by Yuthika and Arvind at their apartment in Empire Tower, a high rise in a posh locality of the city. Both of them looked very terrified.

Raj conducted an EMF session after switching off the electrical appliances and observed high spikes in most areas of the apartment. It was quite obvious that the place was haunted. So, he asked the Mumbai team to reach Bengaluru the next evening. Only Meghna and Siddharth could make it, as the others were busy. They reached Empire Tower straight from the airport. The three of them got straight to work after exchanging pleasantries and meeting the clients. Raj had informed them about the urgency of the situation and his observations as well.

Siddharth, an expert at audio anomalies, began an EVP session, walking around every corner of the apartment. Meghna began taking as many photographs as she could while Raj switched on his night vision video recorder and attempted to initiate an intelligent communication, like Siddharth was doing in another part of the place. It was past midnight and they were conducting the investigation with the lights switched off.

'Can we talk?' Siddharth tried to initiate communication with the entity while inspecting one of the bedrooms, holding his EVP recorder, which he used very proudly because Gaurav had gifted it to him after one of their many successful cases. Gaurav had given it to him saying, 'Your birthday is coming up, right? I know if I had to gift you anything, it better be something useful, something you will use and always treasure for the years to come.'

Flashes of his mentor used to often appear before Siddharth's eyes during such investigations—how Gaurav used to lead from the front, his attentive face, his body language, the way he conducted himself and inspired others. Gaurav was a different person when you met him personally and a complete professional at work. These qualities distinguished him from many others who had followed him and set up other such organizations. However, the way some of these organizations worked irked Gaurav, as he thought that they weren't doing it right. Among the many things his team members learnt from Gaurav was that, whatever they do, they should always represent the field of paranormal research in the best possible way.

'Is there anyone here?' Siddharth repeated, bringing himself back to the present and continuing to attempt communication.

'We are here to help,' he whispered loud enough for the entity to hear.

Suddenly, he heard utensils clinking in the kitchen. As Siddharth moved towards the door, it shut with a bang. The lights came on and began flickering.

'So, you want to tell us something,' he said, looking around to see if there was anything that the entity wanted him to see. But there was nothing. Just a signal that it existed and was very much there.

'Please speak to us,' he requested.

Raj had opened the door by then and entered the room. The lights continued to flicker as Meghna joined them and took photographs, but the battery of her camera drained in a few seconds. There is a theory that spirits need energy to manifest themselves and batteries are a concentrated source of energy, so, it's easy for them to drain energy from the batteries in order to manifest.

'What's your name?' Siddharth asked as Raj and Meghna stood behind him. A lamp in the room moved from one corner to another as if someone dragged it to indicate their presence. The ticking sound of the clock stopped and when they looked at it, they realized it had stopped working. Then, the lights went off leaving them in pitch darkness. Siddharth tried to switch on a torch but couldn't.

There was pin drop silence coupled with an eerie feeling as if someone else was with them in the same room. They could feel a presence and it wasn't good. In the midst of the darkness, suddenly, the television switched on and they saw a random pattern of static in black and white dots. The television was making noises but not the kind that you hear normally—there was something more to it. The three of them went a little closer and listened.

'MURDER. MURDER. MURDER,' they heard a voice coming from the television.

After all, static is only the result of radiated electromagnetic noise picked up by the antenna and ghosts are but energies who can communicate through various mediums.

After a few seconds, the lights came on again and they were joined by Yuthika and Arvind.

'Let's take a break,' Yuthika said, offering them coffee and snacks. While Raj and Meghna accompanied the couple for the late-night refreshments, Siddharth decided to analyse the EVP recordings.

He joined them twenty minutes later and shared his observations, 'There was a suicide in this apartment almost ten years ago.'

Then, he played an audio and said, 'This one should be

clear for everyone, not just me.'

The audio began, '*Goli maar doo!* (I shoot)', a rather hoarse voice could be heard saying clearly, albeit with some interference.

'Most of the other sentences are in reverse. That's how entities communicate in some instances. So, I need to play it back to decipher what they are communicating,' Siddharth's eyes twinkled as he clarified. Quite obviously, he loved what he loved doing.

It was understood that a person with a criminal record used to reside in the same apartment many years ago. The entity didn't tell them everything but communicated that he had died by suicide after his family members had deserted him.

'Suicides can be painful after death. One may get stuck in the same location for ages and keep repeating what they did when they were alive. The characteristics of an entity remain the same as they were when he or she lived. Then, there are the ones who are confused about whether they are dead or alive, ones who don't want to accept the reality,' Meghna explained to Yuthika and Arvind. They listened to the team patiently.

'We will need to cleanse this place,' Raj informed after a pause.

'Cleansing? You mean, some kind of rituals?' Arvind held Yuthika's hands tightly. His wife was terrified and so was he. Someone had to try and act or behave stronger.

'Not at all! Our way is different and does not resort to

religious practices. Our aim is simple—empathize with the dead because they lived once too. What we do is communicate and tell them that neither they nor you will cross the boundary and cause any harm to each other. It's important that the balance between them and us is maintained,' Meghna explained, smiling reassuringly.

The team spent the rest of the night in the living room and could only catch up with some sleep past 4:00 a.m.

In the morning, Arvind called the broker who had sold them the apartment. The broker informed them that someone, indeed, had died by suicide in that flat ten years ago. He also confirmed that the man who had ended his life had a criminal record. But, he had pleaded guilty to everyone—the law, society and his family members. He had said that he was being framed by someone and had not been at fault, but he couldn't prove it. Nobody listened. He had been imprisoned for a year after which he had gotten out on bail. However, by then, his wife had left with their two children. She had also filed for divorce and had decided to get remarried; worse still, his wife had gotten full custody of their children. The man had become a victim of acute depression and, over the next few months, had isolated himself inside the apartment. If neighbours are to be believed, a few days before his suicide, he had lost his sanity. One of them had visited the man to talk with him so that he would feel better, but the man had simply repeated, 'Goli maar doo! Goli maar doo!' There wasn't a chance that he had been drunk as per the neighbour and he had reported the matter to the man's wife, too, since he had her number. But, she had clearly told him that she had nothing to do with the man anymore. The next day, the man had been found dead in his apartment, his cold body hanging from the ceiling fan in one of the bedrooms.

Since then, the apartment had been put on rent several times, but none of the tenants had managed to live there for more than a few months because of the paranormal experiences. Finally, it had been decided to sell the flat off at a throwaway price. That's how Arvind and Yuthika had gotten the great deal on this flat.

Arvind and Yuthika decided to moved out of the apartment. They warned the broker that if he did not refund their down payment, they would sue him. He obliged and was extremely sorry for mis-selling the property. IPS never recommends anyone to move out of their house because it is haunted. But, in this case, the couple had been adamant about moving.

Raj contacted the couple a month later to understand if they were still being haunted. Often, an entity can latch onto people even after they leave a haunted place. But, there was no such report from them. The apartment is still vacant and people in the society refrain from crossing it or going near the door. The two families occupying the two other flats on the floor had also been contemplating moving out the last time the IPS team checked on the society over the phone.

❧

Meghna listened to Ekta patiently as she shared her experience. So far, only Gautam had experienced the paranormal in their new house, but, slowly, other family members were experiencing incidents that had no logical explanation. Meghna knew it was time for her to start investigating her own apartment, but, strangely, neither had she come across anything yet, nor had she felt anything, which was quite common for her when she visited supposedly haunted houses. But, in her own home, she was not sensing anything while her brother and sister, who were more of non-believers, were totally terrified. It was quite a dilemma to start with: why would the entity or entities in her own home not communicate with her as well?

The next morning, she enquired with their neighbours about the place, but they dismissed it, saying that there had been no such incidents in the society so far. In the evening, when Meghna returned from work, she met Milind, one of the night-time security guards. He told her that he and his colleagues had been facing certain unnatural occurrences. They heard their names being called out several times and when they looked around, there was nobody. One night, Milind had even been pushed by someone at around 3:00 a.m., when he had been doing his rounds. Then, he had felt like he was being choked for a few seconds and he had sensed a very heavy presence around him as if there was no air to breathe. He had a family to run and couldn't search for another job easily; so, he stuck around and tried to stay in one place at the night.

Another night, a little past 1:00 a.m., when he had felt extremely sleepy and dozed off for a few minutes in his seat, a lady's voice had woken him up, 'Milind! Milind.'

He had opened his eyes to see a woman he had never seen in the society before. However, since he was on night duty, it was possible that she lived there and he had just not seen her until then.

'So late... which flat? All okay, ma'am?' he had asked groggily, standing up still half-asleep. He normally slept during the day and reported for duty in the evening, but, that day, he had to visit a bank to transfer some money to his family back in Ratnagiri.

The woman hadn't spoken a word. She had simply smiled.

'Yes, ma'am?' Milind had repeated, getting back to his senses by now.

Again, she had just given him a wide-eyed smile, without batting an eyelid.

'Yes?' Milind had asked again, raising his voice a little.

Her smile had widened a little more.

'All okay, Milind?' the night gatekeeper had called him, standing a few metres away, near the gate. Obviously, he had also been disturbed out of his sleep.

'Ma'am isn't rep—' Milind had been cut off mid-sentence.

'Who are you even talking to?' the gatekeeper had growled.

Just then, the smiling woman had disappeared into thin air in front of Milind's eyes.

'It can take various forms, Meghna ma'am,' Milind informed Meghna.

Two nights after that incident, he had seen the same woman walking around in the lobby. He had held a copy of Hanuman

Chalisa in one hand and had started reading from it while approaching the place with trembling feet.

'Sankarsuvankesarinandan tejprataapmahajagabandan,' he had chanted, stammering in fear. It had been cold outside and he had been sweating in terror. But he knew that if there was evil, there was a God, too.

The woman had stopped, looked at him and smiled again, like she had the other night. The next second, the entity had transformed into a man—the same smile on his face, the same stare. He had not said anything but simply stood there, looking at Milind.

'I'm leaving tomorrow, ma'am. I've got a new job. This place... it is haunted. It's not good... not good,' Milind told Meghna.

There was so much at stake for Meghna because her family had moved to a new place, which was haunted. She had to do something before it was too late. She had to.

EIGHT

The Other Side of the Mirror

Adarsh Singhania owned a few tea estates in Assam, apart from managing other family businesses too. He had approached IPS through his personal assistant for a very peculiar case at the Naharjan Tea Estate near Dibrugarh, a small city in Assam. The team headed there at once. Obviously, there was no way for any of them to conduct a pre-investigation for this case, as none of the team members lived anywhere close to Assam. So, they decided to travel to the place together. Mr Singhania was to bear the cost of travel, and they would be putting up at the bungalow that they had to investigate.

Tea garden life is different, away from the hustle bustle of urban life. The nearest town is often several kilometres away from a tea estate. Needless to say, there aren't many amenities, especially because people from cities are so used to the supposedly good life. It is a world of its own, with a strong sense of history—the legacy of the British Raj and its tea planters, who introduced them to the country and ran almost all the tea estates before passing on their way of living, all of which adds to its old-world charm.

Mr Tapan Baruah, who was the manager in Naharjan Tea Estate, welcomed the IPS team at the main gate and escorted them in his car from there. He could easily make out that it had been a rough drive for them from Dibrugarh airport. Although it is just thirty-two kilometres away, more than half of the road journey is a bumpy and dusty ride along the old road that had fallen out of repair.

'Phew! It took us two hours to reach! At least, in Mumbai, you know you are going somewhere. Here, it was so dark all around,' Rith informed Mr Baruah, when asked about their experience.

'I know. I know. My sister lives in Andheri. We went there two years ago. But, I must tell you, we couldn't live like that either. You see, when you are amidst nature and have grown up and lived in a certain environment, it becomes very difficult to adjust. So, I can feel you!' he responded with a smile, opening the car window and letting the fresh air in.

'Unpolluted... almost. Breathe in and feel it. You will not get this in the cities,' he told them, driving on the bumpy road.

'How's your daughter now?' Meghna asked.

'The usual,' he replied, with a tinge of sadness.

The team had come to Naharjan Tea Estate for Tapan Baruah's fourteen-year-old daughter. Rina wasn't a normal girl as per the people and society judging her. She was undoubtedly an introvert, always preferring solitude over social gatherings. If there was a party, she would prefer staying at home. Rather than going to the club house, where the tea estate parties were held, she would invite her close friends to her bungalow to share mocktails and appetizers while watching a feel-good movie together. But, she hardly had any friends. As is the case on tea estates, she studied in a boarding school in Darjeeling, as education is a big issue in such places, where there are no good schools even in the nearest town. She came home for four months every year during the winter vacations. But, children her age socialized a lot more. They participate in what is known as 'club culture' on tea estates. Such clubs are mostly used to play golf along with hosting monthly or fortnightly parties and running a tea estate or factory. These clubs run like a *burra* bungalow or the manager's bungalow. Clubs don't have full-time kitchens and the *burra memsaabs* run an amateur catering service that could put a master chef to shame. They would probably spend as much time polishing up their menu for the golf tournaments or parties, as their husbands would on perfecting their putts. Many of the people working on a particular cluster of tea estates contribute to a common fund for the smooth functioning of the club in their area, which is mostly under the jurisdiction of the biggest tea estate among them. Usually a burra memsaab from one of the member tea estates takes the responsibility of the food and drinks for an event and it is another burra memsaab's responsibility for the next one and so on. Even when there is no party, the club is still operational and people working there can visit it for meetings, whereas their children can catch up over snacks and drinks, if they are of age.

But, Rina wasn't interested in any of this. She simply stayed at home, read books, watched television and, most importantly, spent time with her cocker spaniel Lucy, her best friend. Rina's parents tried hard to ask her to accompany them for the Saturday evening parties, but she wouldn't budge. The first incident had happened on one such night.

∾

'I enjoy it here, papa. It's just that I can't pretend to like something I don't. It just shows on my face and you two get embarrassed,' Rina explained to her father rationally and escorted her parents to the veranda outside the main door. Her parents were all decked up for the evening. This party was the responsibility of another burra memsaab, so, Mrs Baruah was at ease. Otherwise, she would have left earlier to manage the arrangements.

Mr and Mrs Baruah returned by 12:10 a.m. that night. They had tried calling Rina at around 10:00 p.m. to enquire if she had eaten her dinner, but the call had gone unanswered.

'She might have fallen asleep,' Tapan told his wife as they proceeded towards the bar for one last round of drinks with colleagues, after which there was a buffet dinner to attend.

The clubhouse wasn't too far away from the Baruahs bungalow, but it was dark and the road was terrible. So, the couple took some time to reach home. The night guard had dozed off and it was only after a few honks of the car that he woke up with a jolt, realizing he was in for a scolding. Luckily, Tapan was more concerned about his daughter and didn't want to waste time on reprimanding a man who otherwise did his duty to the best of his ability.

When the couple reached inside, they noticed that the power had been cut and the house was dark—a very normal thing in tea estates.

'The inverter isn't working, Saab,' the night guard informed as he opened the car doors for the couple.

'Check again,' Tapan told him and knocked on the door, realizing it was open.

'See! Why would Rina not lock herself? Do you know how unsafe it can be here?' he frowned as if his wife didn't know how unsafe it was. But, he had to express it somehow. It was worrisome indeed.

'Rina!' he called for his daughter as they entered the living room.

In that darkness, they saw Rina seated in front of the fireplace, radiant in the golden light of the flame. She sat still on the floor with her face turned towards it.

'Rina,' Tapan walked towards his daughter and called her again.

No response. Not even a tilt of her head.

The air felt heavy, or so Tapan felt, as he approached Rina and tapped her shoulder.

'Ri—'

'Papa,' Rina called for him from behind. Tapan turned around in astonishment. Indeed, his daughter was standing behind him. He turned towards the fireplace and there was nobody!

The lights came on the next second. Tapan and his wife were frightened to say the least but it was only the beginning.

Over the course of the next few days, strange things started happening in the bungalow. Rina's mother fell very sick all of a sudden and had to be rushed to the town hospital; their dog, Lucy, wouldn't enter the house and stayed in the veranda and could be heard barking at odd hours at night— not bravely but out of fear. Tapan had terrible nightmares almost every day in which he saw his wife and daughter being slaughtered. And Rina's behaviour changed. She had always kept to herself, but, now, she would mostly lock herself in her room the entire day. In the evenings, when her father came home from work, he would try to strike up a conversation with her but she would shout at him or show no interest. In a week's time, Rina's mother returned home from the hospital. She felt strange everywhere in the house as if something inexplicably negative was around her all the time. The atmosphere in the house was getting worse and the happy family was happy no more. Strangely, Tapan felt much better when he left the bungalow for work every morning. The moment he was out of the premises, he sensed it instantly. Even the house staff had similar experiences—the cook complained that Mrs Baruah had abused her for no reason one morning although Mrs Baruah was sure that she hadn't even met her then and had been in the flower garden, instructing the gardener. But why would the cook lie? The night guard informed Tapan that he had seen Rina sleepwalk several times. Once, he had dozed off for a few seconds and when he opened his eyes, he was shocked to see her standing where he sat, staring at him. When he asked her if she was okay, she moved away and headed back to the bungalow. A number of such incidents were the reason why Tapan called Mr Singhania and informed him that he wanted to resign.

'Are you crazy? I can't lose a gem of an employee like you for some... some stupid belief... whatever you call that!' he told Tapan.

'Sir, I didn't believe in these things either until recently.'

'You stay there. I'll see what can be done,' Mr Singhania said, calling his personal assistant to discuss the matter. He hadn't ever faced an issue like this. What if the news spread in the nearby areas and market? It was the only productive tea estate he had and Tapan Baruah was an employee he was extremely confident about. The tea business runs on people who know how to manage the labourers and Tapan was wonderful at what he did.

Subsequently, the IPS was entrusted with safeguarding the goodwill of Naharjan Tea Estate, which was a frontrunner in manufacturing tea in Assam.

'I'd like to meet your daughter personally first,' Meghna told Tapan while the team got ready for the night. They were very tired but knew there was no time to waste.

'Don't know if she is in the mood to meet anyone, but

you can try,' Tapan showed her the way to Rina's bedroom.

'Mr Baruah, all this began with her. Trust us, and we can help you as quickly as possible,' Meghna said.

'That goes without saying, Ma'am. Do it your way.'

Rina was reading a book when her father knocked and asked her if they should come in.

'Rina, this is Meghna aunty. She wants to meet you. Say "hi",' Tapan smiled and tried his best to make it look effortless.

'Come in,' Rina said. There was something very womanly about Rina, even at her age. Her gaze, voice and mannerisms were not of the kind you would associate with a teenager.

In the meantime, the others started inspecting the bungalow. They split up. While Siddharth and Rith stayed together inside in the house; Mohan joined Raj, who decided they should take a look outside and at the adjoining areas. Meghna would handle the consultation part, and she knew where to start. As soon as she entered Rina's bedroom, her body confirmed what her mind had guessed. The air in the room felt very heavy and she could feel the presence of a very powerful entity there—powerful not in a good way.

'Rina, what do you do when you are alone?' she asked after exchanging some customary pleasantries.

'I read. Sometimes, I watch movies.'

'Wow, which book did you read last?' Meghna asked, looking around, observing a lot to make sense of the situation in the bungalow.

The walls in the room were plastered with posters and images, which indicated that Rina was a total horror freak.

A huge poster of William Friedkin's *The Exorcist* adorned the wall to the left, along with other gothic images inspired by literature and movies.

'Someone is a huge horror fan, eh?' Meghna asked with a smile.

'Yes! I love it. I'm currently reading a horror non-fiction book, too. It is quite a rare edition at that. I'm an active member of various international horror associations and that helps me source such material.'

'Great. Ever seen a paranormal investigation in progress?'

'I was a huge fan of Gaurav Tiwari. I hope you guys continue to keep up the great work.'

'We are doing our best. So, Rina, what happened that night? Really?' Meghna got to the main topic.

'Which?'

'That night, when your parents were away for a party. It all began after that night, right?'

'Nothing,' Rina's answer was as brief as it could be.

'Ever summoned ghosts, Rina?' Meghna held a book she had already spotted during the conversation and showed it to her—a compilation of articles suggesting the various methods of summoning the dead through séances, with Ouija boards or even without them.

The expression on Rina's face changed from cluelessness to surprise to one of taking responsibility for what she had done.

'You can tell me, Rina. I promise I won't tell your parents,' Meghna promised her, holding her hands.

A complete horror freak, Rina was very curious about everything supernatural. A voracious reader, she mostly kept to herself and found solace in books about ghost stories, true incidents of possessions and exorcisms—basically, anything related to the horror genre that she so loved. She had been a different child and had taken time to socialize. She hated being in the midst of people. She was lonely and had no friends in her boarding school.

That night had not been the first time that she had summoned a spirit. She had done it at school when nobody had been in the dormitory, especially during the short holidays, when most girls left, but it wasn't wise for her to travel all the way to Assam. However, nothing had happened when she had done such things at school. So, she had done it again at home. She had called them—the outsiders who live around us and are as real as we are.

'How did you summon them?' Meghna probed further.

'The mirror is a good way to communicate with them,' Rina confessed.

⁇

That night, when her parents were away, Rina lit a few candles and turned off all the lights in the big bungalow. Once there was enough wax, she splashed the large antique mirror in her room with it. Sprinkling salt around the mirror and herself, she set up the candles around her and kept as quiet as she could. The process had already begun. Once the wax on the mirror had dried, she took a knife and carved in it the type of spirit she wanted to summon—a witch.

'Witches living through time. I'm in need of assistance,' she said.

She paused for a second and repeated it.

'Oh spirit, come, I beckon you. Share your story, come until the morning light,' she concluded the ritual and sat silently in the big, dark bungalow, listening to her own breathing, synchronized with the beating of her heart.

'Nothing. Again,' she stood up after a few minutes to switch on the light but failed.

'Anyone here?' she asked.

Silence.

'Any—' she was interrupted.

'Yes,' someone whispered in her ears and the candles were blown off all at once by a gust of wind that obviously hadn't come from outside the bungalow since all the doors and windows were locked.

∽

Meghna asked Rina to stay with her parents in the living room. Then, she met Siddharth and Rith.

'Any leads?' she asked.

'The entity is in no mood to communicate, but there are traces of very high activity in some areas. We have marked the hotspots,' Siddharth said.

'Haven't Raj and Mohan returned yet?'

The night guard rushed inside frantically and let out a howl of anguish, like he had seen something that he wouldn't be able to erase from his memory soon.

'Saab! Dead bodies!' he exclaimed, in no state to talk properly, but Tapan could make out that he had come to call him. Raj and Mohan were waiting for them in the flower garden.

Usually, the team switches off their mobile phones during investigations so that EMF meter readings can be genuine. So, the guard had to call the others to witness their discovery.

The EMF and K-II meters had been spiking at an all-time high in a particular area of the garden. So, Raj had asked the night guard to share anything that he was aware of, but he wasn't.

'Dig this place,' Raj had said.

'But—' the guard had begun protesting, but Raj had interrupted him.

'Just dig.'

It had rained very heavily that morning, and the soil had been wet, which had made it easier for the guard to dig the ground. Although this wasn't his job, the gardener wouldn't have been available at that hour, and it would have taken him too long to get there from his village.

The guard had been digging for a few minutes when they had observed something. Raj had flashed his torchlight and gone closer.

'It's the crown of a skull!' he had remarked, pointing at it. Mohan had come closer too.

'Yes,' Mohan had confirmed as the guard had continued digging, his hands trembling.

'Someone was buried here,' Raj had commented and asked the guard to call the others.

'Let's go,' Tapan stood up to follow the guard and the others joined him too. As soon as they got to the main door, it banged shut and wouldn't open. The lights went off and all of them could hear someone humming. The sound was coming from Rina's bedroom, but she was with them. Tapan held his wife and daughter as tightly as he could—the guard screamed at the top of his voice while Meghna grappled in the darkness to light a candle. Once they had a source of illumination, she led the way to the bedroom.

'It's all—' Rina cried, about to confess.

But Meghna interrupted her, 'Shhh, we will sort this out,' she told them as they approached the door and opened it slowly. After all, she had made a promise to Rina, and Rina's parents would be most disappointed if she confessed.

When they reached Rina's room, a pungent smell, like that of rotting eggs, met their nostrils. The air around them felt very heavy. Meghna's EMF meter spiked to its highest point as she handed over the candlestand to Rina so that she could hold her infrared night vision camera to photograph the entity.

'I'm all ears if you want to talk,' Meghna said loudly.

The lights came on and the bulb in the room flickered and exploded the next second. It was dark once again.

Meanwhile, Raj and Mohan were waiting for the others

to join them in the garden, but none of them had turned up.

'Something is wrong, Mohan,' Raj said. He asked Mohan to wait while he sprinted towards the main door of the bungalow. He tried to open it but failed. He pushed as hard as he could and kicked it harder, but it still wouldn't open.

Then, an idea struck him. There was a big possibility that the entity troubling the family belonged to the remains found in the flower garden. Raj just had to burn them and the chances were that the plan would work. He looked around and saw the manager's jeep parked in front of him. He flashed his torchlight on it and started searching for a container and a pipe. He needed fuel.

Meghna and the others inside the bungalow stood still as they heard someone humming once again. It was a lady, and, whoever she was, the entity was very much present there.

'Show yourself,' Meghna stepped forward and demanded—her voice confident and strong.

The antique mirror towards their left cracked loudly, made all the more louder by the silence and emptiness of the bungalow.

Rina, her parents and the night guard screamed in terror as a lady's face appeared on the other side of the mirror. It wasn't too clear at first, but, as they stared at it for a few seconds, they could make out the facial features. Meghna, Siddharth and Rith stood in front of the others, guarding them as they looked at the mirror and saw the face disappear. The humming resumed.

Meanwhile, Raj got hold of a jerry can from the garage and looked around for a pipe. Finally, he found a water hose pipe, which the gardener used to water the flower and vegetable gardens. He dipped one end of the pipe into the tank of the parked car and put the other end into his mouth first and sucked till he felt the petrol. Then, he removed the pipe, closed the end with his finger and placed it into the jerry can while removing his finger. The fuel started flowing into the can. Raj, always known for his daredevil approach, had done this at the risk of ingesting gasoline. But, this was the only way that had come to his mind in the moment. Once the can was full, he sprinted back to the flower garden, where Mohan was waiting for him.

'Where are they?' he asked, seeing nobody with him.

'Now, they will come or we can go in,' he said with a smile and poured the fuel on the remains.

Then, he took out a lighter from his pocket and lit it.

'It kills, really,' he said, looking at Mohan while burning the remains. Flames erupted into the night as they stepped back from the burning remains. All the lights in the bungalow began flickering, as if mocking the darkness.

Meghna, Siddharth, Rith and the others inside heard a loud wailing sound while the cracks in the mirror intensified till the large glass shattered and fell on the floor. The next second, everything was normal again. The lights came back on, the air around them felt okay and the main door could be opened. Raj and Mohan ran in to check on everyone.

The team hugged each other and all of them understood

that this case had been quite bizarre and had impacted all of them significantly.

'But how did it all happen?' Tapan asked them as they sat in the living room, having the famous Assam tea.

'Don't bother about it, Tapan. Things happen,' Meghna smiled, looking at Rina. This would be their little secret.

Rina is still in touch with Meghna. She is a little more sensible now, although just as curious about the supernatural.

∽

Despite everything that had been going on in Meghna's life, her work didn't stop and neither did she want it to. The brief lull after Rev. Tiwari's death couldn't deter the IPS from living up to what India's first paranormal research society stands for—helping people in need of consultation and investigation. Contrary to what it had been like when Gaurav had been with them, many of their cases now were based out of the team's base locations. Gaurav had lived in Delhi and, along with solving cases in the city and nearby areas with Raj, he had also travelled to other parts of the country and abroad.

When he had founded IPS in 2009, the first few months had been spent in travelling to various cities and towns to recruit people who had an inclination to join him and know about the 'unknown'. Over the course of years, many had left the organization, but some had stayed and others had joined later.

Within a few years, the team had been set with people he could blindly trust and count on. But, they rarely had to go out of their base locations for the investigations. Gaurav had taken care of that by travelling on their behalf. Raj used to accompany him on many of these cases, especially in Rajasthan and parts of North India. It was different now, though, and the team is more mobile when it comes to taking up cases.

❧

NINE

The Voice from Afterlife

Almost two months after the case in Assam, the IPS team got an important outstation case again in Corgao, a village in the Pernem district of North Goa. Although Raj and Mohan couldn't make it for the case, Rith joined Meghna and Siddharth on the second day of the investigation. He had a prior commitment with the radio station he worked at and there was no way he could skip it.

Meghna and Siddharth boarded a train from Chhatrapati Shivaji Maharaj Terminus to Pernem followed by another from Pernem to Corgao. After a tiring, almost thirteen-hour-long journey, they reached the village. Martin Coutinho, the man who had reached out to them regarding the various unnatural incidents taking place in his home, was there to pick them up at Corgao station. Their destination was another thirty minutes away from there, and he knew that getting a cab would be a hassle for them. Moreover, Martin wanted to get to know the team before they reached the house and tell them about everything that had been happening.

The countryside unfolded before Meghna and Siddharth, like a divine fingerprint, curving and changing constantly—no two parts were the same. The creator had made this part of the world with a unique view—the dip and sway of the land, the patterns and species of flora, the ever-changing sky and wind. In the expanse of green, there were more hues than anyone could ever name, and the sight was a sheer delight for sore eyes that were accustomed to dreary city life.

Martin Coutinho was in his mid-forties, and while he was a man of few words, he needed to talk that day.

'It all began after my wife's death a few months ago,' he told Meghna and Siddharth while driving to the village.

'Soon after our marriage, I realized she had problems—many of them,' Martin informed Siddharth and Meghna.

'What kind of problems?' Siddharth asked, looking at the rear view mirror to look at Martin. Martin looked into it too, and their eyes met.

'She was clinically depressed and very unhappy with everything in life. It all began when we were about to be parents for the first time, but Angela gave birth to a stillborn baby. After that, she started losing her mind slowly. Although I tried my best to keep her happy, it was never enough. It didn't help that we had three children over the next ten years. Occasionally, she used to be normal. But then, there used to be times that baffled us and made us question her mental state. Suddenly, she would wake up in the middle of the night and start searching for something. Sometimes, we would be discussing something and she would seem okay and then, she would go completely blank and start staring at the ceiling, just like that. She would scold the children for no reason and even beat them at times. I was certain that they were not safe with their mother. So, I hired a nanny who would care for them when I wasn't around.'

'You must have consulted a doctor,' Siddharth said.

'Oh, yes. Of course, I did. Our family doctor recommended that I take her to a psychiatrist in Panaji. I used to visit him once a month with Angela for her sessions. She was also prescribed medication, which I ensured she didn't miss taking. But, you know what, when I delved deeper into her past, I learnt that she had shown symptoms of depression since her childhood,' Martin said, stopping the car. 'We are here,' he said, parking the car on the muddy road outside his house.

Contrary to what Meghna and Siddharth had thought, the house was quite modern and well-maintained. It was the biggest one in the locality, which felt like a quaint little town, even though it was a village.

The house was welcoming, from the open door to the wide hallway. The walls were adorned with the photographs of the three children, who were obviously well-loved. The old-fashioned parquet was a blend of deep, homely browns and the walls were painted the greens of summer gardens meeting a bold white baseboard. The banister was a twirl of a branch, tamed by a carpenter's hand, its grain flowing in waves of comforting woodland hues. Under the lamplight, it looked like nature's art, something that soothed the soul. Nothing about the house felt wrong or haunted. The three children greeted Meghna and Siddharth and exchanged smiles as Martin led them to their rooms. Rith would be joining them the next day and Siddharth would share one room with him.

Meghna and Siddharth started getting ready for the first round of investigation in the evening. They had unpacked their equipment and already discussed the plan between themselves. While prepping, Meghna decided to ask Martin some more questions, 'How did Angela die?'

'Postpartum hemorrhage. She died due to excessive bleeding. She wanted a fourth child and was adamant. I always tried my best to keep her happy. I told you, right?' he said.

'And the last question before we proceed: what exactly are you facing here?' Siddharth asked.

The pre- and post-investigation consultations are most important in a paranormal investigation for the IPS. While the first indicates the nature of the case so the team can be prepared to solve it, the second helps the client understand the situation and shows them how to cope with it.

'We hear knocks on the main door at the same time—1:10 a.m.—every day. Three knocks, a brief pause, three knocks again. This continues for some time. I have often mustered up all my courage and opened the door but found nobody.'

'Chances of a prank?'

'Who would play a prank every day at that hour of the night, and, that too, in a place like this, where people are few and fast asleep by late evening?'

'We ask this because, strangely, we see or sense nothing unnatural here. Let us begin our work and we will keep you updated,' Meghna told Martin and looked at his three daughters, the eldest of whom looked like she was around thirteen years old.

'Stay with your papa, little girls,' she instructed them with a smile.

This was one of those baffling cases for the team. Nothing happened for the first few hours of their investigation—no EMF meter spikes, no EVP audio anomaly, no apparition, no images, no sound, sense or sight whatsoever, and, most importantly, no communication. Zilch.

'When are your other team members coming here?' Martin asked Siddharth and Meghna during dinner. Ideally, in the village, they ate latest by 9:00 p.m. and, thereafter, went to bed, but that night was different, so, they had a late dinner at 11:00 p.m.

'Tomorrow,' Meghna replied.

'No, no. He is on the way. Look!' Siddharth had switched on his mobile phone and there was a WhatsApp message from Rith, sent at 4:30 p.m.

Wrapped up the show, mate! Boarding the train in some time. Should reach early tomorrow morning.

'Guess we can expect him by early morning,' he told her.

'I'll go and pick him up, too. Don't worry,' Martin said, offering them some more *xitti kodi* (Goan fish curry).

While Martin and his daughters tried to get some sleep after dinner, the team resumed their work a little after midnight, but the first thirty minutes or so yielded no result again.

Just when Siddharth was about to conclude that the house wasn't haunted, the EMF meter spiked! At the same time, the clock struck one. The air around them started feeling a little heavy. Siddharth quickly switched on his favourite equipment, the EVP recorder, again.

'Do we have someone here?' he asked, repeating the question thrice. But, there was no response.

'Let's put it this way. Is there anything you want to tell us? We want to listen to you,' he probed further.

The EMF meter stopped spiking and the air around them felt normal again.

'It's gone,' Meghna whispered.

KNOCK. KNOCK. KNOCK.

Martin and his daughters came rushing out of the bedroom. Obviously, none of them had fallen into a deep slumber.

KNOCK. KNOCK. KNOCK.

The EMF meter spiked to its highest point, indicating very high paranormal activity.

Siddharth switched on his EVP recorder.

'We can talk,' he said softly.

'Just drive the spirit out of the house and our lives! There is no need for communication,' Martin screamed.

'Sir, please let us do our duty,' Siddharth requested, continuing his questions.

The knocks continued for the next few minutes, but no intelligent communication was established.

'We need to inspect all the rooms properly again. There is something it wants to tell us. I can sense it,' Meghna told Siddharth. They split ways to save time. Martin and the children sat together in the living room, knowing they wouldn't be sleeping that night.

After another three hours of inspecting each and every room in the house, Meghna and Siddharth found nothing.

Meghna wanted to conclude the investigation with the team's few findings, as she and Siddharth were on the verge of wrapping up. Martin's daughters had dozed off by then on the sofas in the living room. Martin tried his best to stay awake, guarding them.

Meghna said to him, 'We must tell you this, Martin. Although an entity exists here, it means no harm to you. The investigation hasn't yielded any concrete results so far, but there is something it wants to tell us.'

Everything about Martin felt heavy, from his arms to his feet. His head lolled from one side to another, eyes nearly closing. Then, suddenly, a part of his consciousness seemed to awaken with a jolt.

'Did you hear us?' Meghna asked.

'I'm responsible for her death. I killed her,' Martin

confessed, sitting up straight.

The next moment, his expression changed and he looked extremely puzzled. Meghna and Siddharth observed that something about him didn't seem right.

'I killed her,' Martin kept repeating, looking totally confused.

'Martin,' Meghna called out to the man.

'Angela. It's Angela,' Martin said, but his voice sounded strange—full of rage. His eyes had a different gaze, full of immense anger.

Then, Martin looked bewildered again as if he had no clue what was going on with him. There he was, sitting in the living room, confessing his sins without wanting to, and a strange force seemed to be making him do it.

'Confess, you bastard,' Martin's eldest daughter said, in the same strange and angry voice he had spoken in a few minutes back.

Martin screamed in terror and stood up. His daughter kept staring at him with eyes wide open, her gaze different and full of rage. He knew that gaze. He had seen it. He had lived with it for fifteen years. It was his wife, Angela, whose death he had been responsible for.

A few minutes later, Martin cried his heart out in front of his three children, Meghna and Siddharth and kept saying, 'I wanted a son. I wanted a son.'

∽

Martin moved out of Corgao after his graduation to build a career. For a year, he worked as a cashier in one of the small restaurants on Baga beach, but, soon, he realized that the opportunities there would be restricted. So, he moved to Mumbai and worked in various organizations, mostly off-roll jobs related to selling insurance, loans and credit cards. Nothing great really happened despite him giving his best in a city where sustaining can be immensely difficult. Frustrated by the limited growth during his seven years in Mumbai, he decided to relocate to his village fifteen years ago. Upon returning, he married Angela in a church in Corgao. It was an arranged marriage, but their families knew each other. The couple started a cashew plantation to earn a living. It wasn't always monetarily productive, but life in the village could be significantly cheaper than a city. They were happy, at least in the first two years of their marriage.

However, Martin had never been a good husband. To start with, he didn't want an arranged marriage. He had been seeing a college-going Hindu Maharashtrian girl during his stay in Mumbai, who was basically his landlord's daughter. But, Martin's parents had opposed the relationship. In fact, it was one of the reasons why he had to come back to his village and settle down. His arranged marriage with Angela was never a happy one. But, it hardly had anything to do with the woman, whose only fault was that she trusted her parents' choice. Angela tried her best to be a good wife but could never keep Martin happy. He resented his decision of not getting married to the girl he loved by taking a stand against his parents. All his frustrations were directed towards his wife—sometimes indirectly and at other times, directly. It was an abusive relationship to say the least and, soon, Angela was suffering from depression. Her mental state deteriorated to the point that she had to start visiting a psychiatrist in Panaji and be on heavy doses of medication.

Amidst all these domestic troubles, Martin wanted a son. But, their first child was a daughter. So, they tried again two years later and had a daughter again. Martin didn't really mistreat his daughters because he didn't want them, but he was adamant about having a son, who would continue his family's legacy. Like most people, Martin's deep-rooted prejudice made him try again, and his wife gave in to her husband's craziness.

To make matters worse, their financial condition wasn't too good. Martin, who had failed to build a corporate career, was a businessman, and living in his ancestral home did help in cutting down a lot of expenses. But Angela knew that bringing up the children was going to be a tough task. She had high ambitions for her daughters and didn't just want to marry them off. But, Martin's madness knew no bounds at times, often devolving to marital rape. A few years later, they had a third daughter. By then, Martin had started blaming Angela for almost everything. He would shout at her more often, mistreat her, even beat her. All this worsened Angela's depression, a condition where she needed solace, but, apart from the smiles on her daughters' faces, there was no respite.

'Let's do it one last time,' Martin came home drunk one night and forced himself on his wife.

Months later, Angela died due to excessive bleeding during delivery. A few hours later, they lost the child, too, due to birth defects. The doctor informed Martin that it had been a boy.

After this family tragedy, Martin was a changed man, or so it appeared. Days passed and he kept brooding over his life, his relationship with his wife, the way he treated her, her death, and their son's death. But, it was too late. All he could do now was try to be a good father to his three daughters, and he really tried hard.

'I'm sorry! I'm sorry!' he howled in agony, as his daughters cried too. The eldest daughter, who was thirteen, and the younger, who was eleven, looked at their father in disgust. The youngest daughter, who was just five, could only make out that her papa had done something really bad.

&

'Shame on you! Even the most severe punishment won't do justice to the torture mom went through with you for fifteen years of her life. Shame on you!' the eldest daughter screamed at her father, tears rolling down her cheeks.

Meghna and Siddharth were moist-eyed too.

'You called us here to drive out the spirit. Now, we understand why you didn't approve of me trying to communicate with her. You got us wrong, Mr Martin. We are investigators who determine the truth and try to strike a balance between the living and the dead, if it's necessary. We don't drive out spirits. Get that right,' Siddharth told him and asked Meghna to pack their bags. He said that they would travel back to Mumbai in the morning. But, they knew that they had to complete their duty. Rith joined them in the morning, and they conducted a cleansing session.

The entity communicated with them a few times, and they agreed upon a balance when the IPS team told her that Martin would take good care of her daughters.

This was one of the cases where the team didn't have a good feeling after closing it successfully.

Siddharth checked with the eldest daughter a year later, 'How are things?' he asked, indicating the situation at home and her relationship with her father.

'Good,' she replied.

Siddharth had no interest in talking to Martin, hence, he had enquired with his daughter. He might be a changed man, but the team felt that Angela should have walked away from him much earlier during their failed marriage. She would still have been a part of the living world and not have to guard her daughters from the other world.

After successfully solving the Naharjan Tea Estate case, the IPS team returned home from Assam the next afternoon. Meghna knew there would be no break for her. She had to investigate

her apartment and the society premises, which couldn't be postponed for a single day. Ekta, Gautam, her mother and everyone else in her family had stayed together, mostly in one room, during the last few days while Meghna had been away. Not much activity had been reported during this time, except for the noises coming from the living room at night. But, the point was, they were now sure that they were living in a haunted house. Meghna had shared this with Siddharth, who wanted to help her find out more.

'Let me do the initial rounds first and thank you for always being so kind and supportive,' Meghna told Siddharth as she got down at Malad. They had boarded the same cab from the airport, and Siddharth dropped her before heading home.

The case in Assam had been tiring, and Siddharth was looking forward for some recreation that night. Maybe, he could listen to some soft music while reading a book or help his mother cook dinner—anything to help him stay away from thinking about the paranormal for a few hours. It was difficult, but he wanted to make an effort that evening.

Meghna reached home, freshened up and unpacked her equipment within an hour. She asked Ekta and Gautam to be with her during the process.

'The entity might want to show and tell me something that may not be true. Different perspectives are always welcome for a successful investigation. And don't worry, I'm here. No need to be scared,' she said reassuringly.

When it comes to real-life paranormal investigations, things don't happen as quickly as they do in movies, which project horror in a different, mostly exaggerated light. One needs to be patient to be able to start a conversation with an entity and get to the crux of the matter. There are times when paranormal investigators spend days and nights trying to establish communication and nothing happens. Then, there are times when intelligent communication is established within a few minutes. It all depends on how interested the entity is in manifesting, if not visibly then at least to the other senses. Paranormal activities may be frequent when the entity wants to make its presence felt. Alternatively, they may take the form of residual hauntings—basically, energy left behind after someone dies traumatically, manifesting through sounds, perhaps footsteps, or even an actual apparition. The entity could be existing in a loop and repeating the actions that happened before its death. Meghna suspected that this was what was transpiring in her apartment. She had to know what happened there. She could only cleanse the house after knowing the story behind the haunting to ensure that her family could live there at peace and the entity/entities there would let them maintain the balance.

Around 8:00 p.m., accompanied by Ekta and Gautam, Meghna commenced the first round of investigation of the place she wanted to call home. But, like many other cases, she could not establish any intelligent communication with the entity/entities for hours. The EMF meter did spike on many occasions, confirming the existence of a presence. However, the many EVP sessions she attempted yielded no results. The many photographs that she took with her night vision camera after switching off the lights didn't help either.

Around 1:00 a.m., Meghna, Ekta and Gautam sat down in one of the bedrooms to share some snacks, as they had skipped dinner.

'What's really going on here, Megs?' Gautam asked, as he was completely baffled about whatever was going on.

Meghna was certain by now that the area was jinxed and so was their apartment. Gautam and Ekta had already experienced the paranormal in the house, and the night guard had also shared his story with Meghna. But, it was difficult for her to determine what was going on. However, she had deduced the type of haunting and knew it would be difficult for her to handle this alone. Without communicating with the unknown, how could she cleanse her house?

'Ever heard about a residual haunting?' Meghna asked, looking at both of them while munching on a biscuit. She was extremely hungry, and it had been a tiring day due to the journey from Assam.

'Nope. Enlighten us, Megs,' Ekta said, curious.

'In layman's language, think of an old film loop or recording. This type of a haunting is like a scene that plays over and over again through the years. An event gets imprinted in the ambient environment or on objects in general—this is a residual haunting. It may discharge and replay on loop, just like a recording. These events may not always be visual. Although both of you have seen some of the actions of the entities here, who are caught in a loop, they can be replayed as smells, sounds, noises, with no apparent explanation. These sounds, visuals and senses relate to the traumatic events that have transpired at the

location. For example, if a murder is committed at a location, that event keeps playing on loop there years after it occurred. The entities that are not at peace keep repeating it, often unsure if they are dead, not wanting to accept the change.'

'How can you be sure that this is a residual haunting?' Gautam asked.

'By listening to the experiences you and the night guard have shared with me. Gautam, each time you were in the midst of it, almost the same things happened. Apparitions are like moving pictures and can usually be seen in the same spots, walking down the same hallway, appearing in the same window, repeating the same motion. They are mostly unaware of the living people around them. Such cases do not have any interaction between the ghost and the witnesses,' Meghna paused and drank some water. She looked at the clock in the room. It was 1:20 a.m.

She continued, 'Strange sounds such as footsteps, voices, knocking are common. Gautam, you mostly heard glasses clinking and people talking to each other. Then, there was the lady who walked to the main door. It repeated the next time too, right? Almost? Another possible sign of a residual haunting is high levels of humidity. Did you feel that it was humid?'

Gautam stared at Meghna for a while and recalled how he had been perspiring during the experiences.

'Yes, but it was cold too. It was a strange feeling, really. It was chilly, it was hot, it was humid,' he recalled.

'Happens! The air around you feels heavier—warm or cold, depends,' Meghna confirmed.

144

Suddenly, all three of them heard music coming from the living room. Someone was playing a violin.

'Shhh,' Meghna indicated to Gautam and Ekta to keep quiet and follow her. She carried her camera with her as she led the way towards the music. She knew that the EVP recorder would be of no use.

As they walked closer to the room, the music became clearer along with the other sounds—people chatting with each other, glasses and crockery clinking. Meghna, Ekta and Gautam walked to the centre of the room and stood there for a few minutes, simply hearing everything that was happening, though not in front of their eyes. The air was heavy around them, and a strange kind of a chill ran down their spines. A party was happening, but they could not see anyone!

Meghna began taking as many photographs as she could, hoping she could capture some anomaly or apparition.

'Where exactly did the lady walk in from?' she asked Gautam.

He pointed at the window where he had seen her. Meghna went near the place.

She zoomed in and... click! There she was! The lady stared back at her with the characteristic wide-eyed smile. She appeared in a flash and disappeared right in front of Meghna's eyes.

'Did you see her?' she turned around to ask Gautam and Ekta, but they were not there!

'Gautam! Ekta!' she called them.

'Yes, Meghna?' Gautam's voice came from exactly where he had been standing a moment ago.

'I don't understand. I—I can't see you two!' she said, her voice tinged with fear. The paranormal investigator in Meghna knew that the entities were playing mind games with her, but she was worried for her siblings.

'What are you saying? We are right here. We can see you, Meghna, what are you saying?' Ekta screamed in fear—the same fear she could also see in Meghna's face, the fear of losing your dear ones.

Suddenly, the violin and people's chatter resumed.

'Would you care for some more dessert?' a lady asked.

'Thank you, Isha. But we need to leave,' another lady responded.

BANG! Suddenly, there was a gunshot! Then another, and another and many more followed.

Meghna looked around in horror, but she couldn't see anyone.

Gautam and Ekta shrieked in terror. Meghna could feel them next to her, but why couldn't she see them?

The music of the violin resumed again. But, now, there were no people chatting, no glasses or crockery clinking. Just the melancholic violin, which sent shivers down Meghna's soul. It was the music of death.

TEN

The Ghost of Esther Brown

Viraj Narang was a first-generation wealthy businessman, born and brought up in Delhi. He and his family had recently purchased a house in Kasauli, a hill station that Leena, his twelve-year old daughter, had loved during a visit.

'Papa, I'd love to just live and laze around here once a year,' Leena had said to her father one day. A few months later, on her birthday, Viraj had gifted her their new holiday home. The house was on the outskirts of the town, a rather secluded place in the hills. Viraj, his wife Radhika and Leena would mostly occupy the house for a month during the summer. At other times, a caretaker would live in the house with another servant to maintain the property. Since the house dated back to the 1930s, its exteriors and interiors had been renovated, as per the broker. It had a fancy, wrought iron gate along with a grey stone compound wall. It was a simple country home—the front door, made of dark wooden planks with black hinges spreading half way across, had the rustic appeal that rich city-folk craved. The interiors had the charm of a rural home with every modern convenience of a penthouse suite.

On a hot summer afternoon, the family reached the house. They would be spending a month in Kasauli. Viraj would travel once a week to Delhi for work, but, besides that, he would be managing the business from the comfortable confines of his new home away from home.

They got down from the car and rang the doorbell, waiting for the caretaker to open the door. Before pressing the intercom, Leena ran her fingers over the rough stone walls, feeling their coolness even in the gruelling heat. She let her eyes absorb the myriad hues of grey. She removed her hand and turned to ring the doorbell again, but as her finger moved forward, the door opened.

Bhagwaan Prasad, the caretaker, greeted them with a wide smile as they walked in.

'How are things, Bhagwaan?' Radhika asked him.

'Memsaab, I was waiting for you to come over here so that I could talk to you in person,' Bhagwaan Prasad responded.

'Yes? Tell me.'

'I can't continue working here. Please let me go.'

'Why, Bhagwaan? What's wrong? You just joined us a month ago!' Viraj exclaimed.

'Saab, this house is haunted!' Bhagwaan's voice quivered.

'Nonsense!' Viraj shouted. He did not believe in spirits and ghosts.

'You want to go, please do. But don't spread such silly rumours about the house,' he chided Bhagwaan.

Despite this grim beginning, four days later, Leena was having the best time of her life in their new house in the hills. Everyone in the family realized that they had so much time for each other. The day would start late, as they wouldn't wake up before 11:00 a.m. They had a great cook, who would prepare an English breakfast for them. After the first meal of the day, Leena would laze around in and around the house or read a book seated on the swing in the spacious veranda. Viraj would catch up on some work on his laptop while Radhika would inspect the various nooks and corners of the house and plan a better design for the house.

On one such afternoon, Leena was reading a book while basking in the sun when she felt that there was someone behind her swing. Someone breathed heavily and Leena noticed a shadow fall across the wall to her left. She turned around to look but didn't see anyone.

'Mom!' she called.

Since her mother wasn't anywhere near her, Leena decided to go in and check on her. She knew that her father would be busy.

'Mom!' she called again as she entered the living room.

What Leena saw there left her numb with fear. A British lady was sitting on their sofa, staring at Leena.

'Leave my house,' she said with a stern glance.

Leena could still try to call her mother, but she knew that her voice wouldn't reach Radhika.

'MOM!' she finally managed to scream, standing there, paralysed with fear, as the British lady vanished into thin air.

∽

After Leena's terrifying experience, Radhika persuaded Viraj to consult a professional. That was when he came across IPS.

'The Gaurav Tiwari one,' he mumbled to himself while looking them up.

'But before we call them, beta, are you sure you didn't imagine it?' he asked Leena, caressing her head.

'I didn't! I didn't imagine it, Papa. Please trust me,' Leena cried.

'This should be genuine. We all know Gaurav Tiwari and his work,' Radhika said, calling one of the mobile numbers mentioned on the website—it happened to be Raj's contact.

Despite the short notice, Meghna and Siddharth flew to Chandigarh the very next day. Raj, who drove from Delhi to Chandigarh, met them there and then, the three of them proceeded to Kasauli together. After a two-hour-long refreshing drive, they reached the house and were welcomed by Viraj and his family at the gate. Rith and Mohan couldn't make it for this one.

For this case, the IPS team knew that a pre-investigation wouldn't be possible, as none of the team members stayed in the hill station. Nonetheless, the team got to work soon after they reached.

'Any other incident apart from the one you mentioned?'

Raj asked as they walked in with the family and sat in the living room, where Leena had apparently seen the spirit.

'No. But my wife, Radhika, did think that she heard voices in the backyard,' Viraj said, looking at his wife to confirm what she had told him earlier that day.

'It's an old house, Mr Viraj. It must have seen a lot,' Meghna told him and asked Siddharth to explain their way of investigating. It is crucial that the client is on the same page as the team before the process begins.

The team got to work an hour later, after freshening up. While Siddharth attempted to communicate with the entity via his EVP recorder from the hotspot i.e., the living room, Meghna began inspecting the house. Raj, with his video camera, explored the area outside and the backyard, a miniature woodland of small trees and native shrubs, trimmed as if they were green flames. The calmness soothed Raj's soul and nothing there seemed to be jinxed. Not till he switched on his EMF meter and it spiked. Haunted places need not always look grim and threatening. Often, an entity exists in a place simply because it is stuck there—not accepting, unsure or unaware of their death.

Siddharth's EVP session established an intelligent communication within an hour or so. It was a spirit that wanted to communicate with the team.

'Please beep once if you are a male, twice if you are a female,' Siddharth requested. Meghna joined him, as there was no activity in other parts of the house.

Beep! Beep!

'Are you the same lady who manifested in this living room the other day? Please beep once for yes.'

Beep!

'Do you want to tell us something?'

Beep!

Thus began a series of questions that both Meghna and Siddharth had in mind to determine the reason behind the haunting.

Around 11:00 p.m., the three of them sat together while Siddharth analysed the voice anomalies recorded during the session.

'Her name is Esther Brown,' Siddharth told Viraj and his family when they caught up after the first round of investigation.

Just then, the clock struck two. They knew this was going to be a sleepless night for all of them.

∞

Kasauli was developed during the peak of the British Empire in India. The British had fallen in love with this village, so they had bought it from the local Rana for five thousand rupees, giving it a new name. It was then set up as a cantonment to garrison troops for war against the Sikhs. The first Anglo-Sikh War happened in 1845. After this, the British felt Kusowlie (that is how they spelt it then) was too serene and beautiful to remain a garrison, so, they developed it as a hill resort. Not as big as Shimla, it still had British visitors during summer.

Indians were not allowed in most places, including the Upper Mall, where the best bungalows stood, the Kasauli Club and other areas, too. Indian people only came in contact with the British in the bazaar, when memsahibs (British women) went shopping. However, things started changing during the Second World War. The sahibs went off to war, leaving their memsahibs, children, nannies, cooks and bearers behind. With them gone for a while, the Indians mustered up the courage to take evening walks on the Upper Mall. By then, the pretty memsahibs were quite lonely and eager to befriend Indians. What began with exchanging greetings, mostly during these evening walks, quickly turned into invitations to lunch or dinner at the memsahib's homes.

Esther Brown was one such memsahib. In 1938, she had moved to Kasauli with her husband, Arthur Brown, who served the East India Company. Newly married, it was her first stay in India, and Kasauli had been an even more beautiful place back then. The house allotted to them was a little on the outskirts of the town, which made life even slower and quieter. It felt great for a year and then, her husband had to leave for the war. Esther tried to find solace in books while he was away. Soon, it was understood that the war would last much longer than it had been first expected, and her husband wouldn't be back till it ended. Esther found herself getting very lonely during this time. She began visiting the Upper Mall for evening walks with her helper, a young local girl the couple had employed. On one of her evening walks, she met Sumer Sharma, a local resident who ran a catering business, which served the East India Company soldiers who lived alone in Kasauli. Sumer was a handsome and smart man who could converse in English. Esther found a friend in him, and their relationship bloomed into something deeper within a few months. They started meeting each other frequently and started spending time at Esther's house. Love happened even before Esther knew it, and they were physically intimate as well. But, Kasauli had been an even smaller place then with even lesser people around. News of their affair soon spread across the hill station.

A few months later, Esther's husband returned to Kasauli and learnt about his wife's extramarital affair with an Indian. Outraged, he strangled his wife to death in the living room of their house. Having seemingly lost his mind, Arthur, then, stepped out into the backyard, screaming, 'My wife is asleep inside. I'll not let anyone come in till I'm here!'

These were Arthur's last words, before he put the gun to his forehead, laughing hysterically while pulling the trigger.

Their local domestic worker came in the next morning, discovered the dead bodies of Arthur and Esther Brown and reported the crime to the authorities.

The house had remained unused for many years after this tragedy. Every person or family that had lived in that house since the incident had been haunted by the ghost of Arthur Brown while the ghost of Esther Brown had always tried to warn them to stay away as she had tried to do with Viraj and his family as well.

∽

'So, what does she want now?' Viraj asked.

'Yes. This is our house now,' Radhika added.

'Initially, we thought that the spirit of Esther Brown is still possessive about this house,' Siddharth paused and looked at the family, listening to him with bated breath.

'But, we were wrong. Esther Brown's spirit wants to warn you of another entity, which is harmful, unlike her,' Siddharth continued.

'Whose?' Radhika asked, incredulous.

'Her husband, Arthur's,' Meghna explained.

'Esther Brown's spirit does not want to drive you out of the house. These entities can be caught in a loop, sometimes, of a traumatic incident. After strangling Esther in the living room, Arthur lost his sanity, ran towards the backyard of the house and screamed in pain before shooting himself. You said you heard noises coming from the backyard, right?' Meghna asked Radhika.

'Yes.'

'Didn't the broker inform you about the haunting?' Meghna enquired for her knowledge.

'The rascal didn't mention anything. I'll sue him,' Viraj replied.

'We should leave first,' Radhika told him.

'That is no solution. We never suggest this to our clients,' Meghna said.

'So, what is the solution then?' Viraj enquired.

'Let us try and cleanse your house,' Meghna responded.

'Where is Leena? She was right behind you,' Viraj said looking at Radhika.

But, their daughter was nowhere to be seen.

'Leena!' Viraj called his daughter, but there was no response.

The clock struck three, and, right then, the lights went off.

'Please find her!' Radhika pleaded in a panic-stricken voice.

'Don't worry, we are still here,' Meghna tried to reassure them while she switched on the flashlight on her phone.

'Team, we need to act fast!' Siddharth said and handed over a full-spectrum camera to Meghna.

Raj had something else in mind. 'There is something not right in the backyard, Meghna. Remember that is where Arthur Brown died. That is where we should check. Siddharth can come with me.'

Viraj and Radhika lit the two electric lanterns at home and frantically started searching for their daughter. Meghna tried her best to ask them to remain calm, but, obviously, the parents were in a different state of mind.

She stayed inside, taking photographs while attempting an EVP session, but there was no communication for the first twenty minutes.

Outside, Raj and Siddharth were conducting another EVP session in the backyard.

It was a cold night, the type of coldness that reaches

the bones. The hills were quiet and the two could hear their breath, their heartbeats and their footsteps when they were not talking.

'Arthur Brown, we want you to communicate with us. We could help,' they said together.

'Uncle!' it was Leena! They could hear her, but she was nowhere to be seen.

'Leena, where are you?' Siddharth asked.

'Please help me!' they heard her voice again. This time, from a distance.

'Arthur Brown, what do you want? Don't play games. Talk!' Raj said furiously.

Then, they heard him.

'My wife is asleep inside. I'll not let anyone come in till I'm here!' he said, laughing hysterically, followed by a gunshot.

Siddharth and Raj stood there, speechlessly looking at each other.

Inside the house, Meghna had been trying her best to communicate with the ghost of Esther Brown.

'Help us, Esther. We know only you can!' she said.

'Give us a hint. Anything!' Radhika shrieked. The parents stood behind Meghna in the living room, the place where Esther had been strangled by her husband.

'He won't let me leave,' they heard Esther's voice. Her spirit wept miserably. She had been imprisoned by her husband's spirit for years in the house.

'Please get us our daughter!' Radhika cried and folded

her hands, pleading with the good spirit.

Silence. A few minutes later, the lights came on.

Arthur Brown's hysterical laughter, his voice and the gunshot had been repeating on loop in the backyard, where Siddharth and Raj stood. It stopped too. Leena came running to her parents the next minute. They hugged each other and cried together.

'Where were you?' Meghna asked her.

'I don't know, really. It was very dark in there. I could see you all but from a distance. I called out for help, too, but none of you could hear me,' she sobbed. Viraj kissed her forehead and hugged his darling daughter, trying hard to provide her some solace when he needed it too.

'We appreciate your work and trust you can cleanse the house, Meghna. But we won't take any risk. We will leave this jinxed place in the morning itself,' Viraj told her as Siddharth and Raj joined them to discuss what must have happened and what they could do.

From whatever they could understand, Esther Brown's spirit must have pleaded with her husband to give Leena back to the family by reassuring him that she was very much inside the house and wouldn't be leaving it.

The IPS team concluded their investigation and shared all their findings with Viraj by the next morning, before they all left the house. The documented mail was used by Viraj when he spoke to the broker, who had mis-sold him the property. Raj contacted the family a few months later and they confirmed that everything was fine. The ghost of

The Ghost of Esther Brown

Esther Brown continues to live in the secluded house on the outskirts of Kasauli, guarded by her husband's spirit in the backyard. The house remains unused as of now.

❧

Back at Meghna's house, the air around her grew heavier as the eerie violin music got louder with each passing second until she had to cover her ears.

'Meghna! Meghna!' Ekta was trying to wake her up.

A baffled Meghna opened her eyes slowly and sat up, looking around to find that she was in her bed.

'How—how did I get here?' she asked.

'What do you mean? It was late night; we were talking in this room and you dozed off to sleep. Don't you remember?' Gautam responded, looking at Meghna in disbelief.

'Were you dreaming?' Ekta asked, passing her a water bottle.

Meghna looked at the clock on the wall. It was 4:40 a.m.

'Such a nightmare,' she said, sighing in relief and turned to look back at Ekta and Gautam.

But they were not there! Meghna was alone in the room, in the midst of complete silence barring the ticking clock.

The next second, she was back in the living room, covering her ears—the violin music was still playing, though not as loudly as it had been a few minutes back or whatever time it had been.

'The entities here are playing mind-games with us. EKTA! GAUTAM!' Meghna stood up and screamed at the top of her voice.

159

The music stopped and an eerie silence cast a pall over the room, so much so that Meghna could hear her own breath and the beating of her heart.

'Ekta! Gau—' she started calling them again.

A chorus of laughter coming from all around Meghna, accompanied by the clinking of glasses and plates, interrupted her.

Then, the lights came on. Ekta and Gautam stood right there in the living room, facing Meghna.

'Where were you all this time?' she hugged them.

'We were right here, Megs. What's going on?' Gautam asked, knowing that an inexplicable force was playing some filthy games with them.

'Let's stick together. Let me try communicating with them once again,' Meghna told them and switched on the EVP recorder.

The session yielded no result and she had to conclude the first phase of the investigation by dawn. But she now knew what she had to do: find out as much as she could about the history of the house so that some kind of a solution could be reached.

Without catching up on any sleep, she called the broker, Mr Gokhale, who had sold them the property, and met him in the morning.

'Look, madam. Every place has a history. There is a death or two or more in every place. Does it mean that every place is haunted?' the broker, a shrewd man in his fifties, asked, his points ready.

'But that does not mean you do not inform customers about a history of haunting in a property before selling it to them,'

Meghna said, looking at him sternly. She was in no mood for a casual discussion by that point.

'Madam, puja karwa lo. Sab theek ho jaaega *(Madam, get a puja done. It will all be okay).*'

'*No. I won't. Don't try to convince me. You know I can sue you, right? Mr Gokhale, tell me more about the place, and, yes, you better be honest,*' *she warned.*

Mr Gokhale knew he couldn't mess with her. He had to tell her whatever he knew.

'*The flat you live in now was a sample flat that we used to show people so that they could get an idea about how the flats would look. You can say we used it like a pre-booking office,*' *Mr Gokhale paused and looked at Meghna, who was listening to him patiently. He briefly wondered if it was worth cooking up some story to pacify her or just tell her the truth—the bitter truth that he knew. He decided to stick to the latter and be honest for a change.*

The complex had been constructed on swampy and marshy land. People who had lived in the area for generations were well-aware of the fact that it had been used for dumping waste. Some say that while cleaning the area before the construction began, the workers had found human and animal bones. Others are of the opinion that most of these are rumours.

❧

Around the time that the construction for the society in which Meghna stayed began, Sagar Awasthi joined the promoter of the building as a manager. Hailing from Jaunpur in Uttar Pradesh, Sagar relocated to Mumbai for better job prospects. A graduate with two years of experience from a small town, he found it extremely difficult to sustain in the initial few months in Mumbai. Sagar tried his best to spend as little as possible in the very expensive city. So, he shared a one-room kitchen flat, with an old friend from his village, in Goregaon. His house wasn't too far away from where he got a decent job, after not being able to stick to two others in the course of five months. His first two jobs had been demanding sales jobs, where he had to be on field to sell credit cards, and he had soon understood this wasn't his forte. Real estate turned out to be fine for him. He began working with Mr Dinesh Kothari, a promoter who operated mostly in Malad and Goregaon areas. It was a far more relaxed job. He rarely had to go out of the office. In fact, in the first few months, there was hardly any work. It was as if he was getting paid for simply going to report his attendance, spending the day roaming around in the area and then, leaving for home in the evening. Kothari wanted his manpower in place before the first phase of the construction, after which he would begin marketing the property and flats that could be sold through brokers and various real estate websites. Sagar's job would be to represent the property and show the premises to the prospective buyers—flats wouldn't be available for possession during the first phase, but a sample flat could be used to give clients an idea.

'It's not what you sell them but how you sell it,' Kothari explained to Sagar one day, taking a good look at him from head to toe.

'*Let's give you a makeover first,*' *he smiled.*

By the next week, Kothari had made Sagar a different man—the small-town image was gone. He wore smartly fitting formal clothes, sported gelled hair and spoke better English or maybe, it sounded better to the ears. Kothari had shared many tips and tricks with Sagar, which he rigorously followed and realized that he had suddenly begun feeling more confident. He also started earning decently, and, by the end of the month, he was saving money, which he hadn't been able to manage earlier. He was also looking forward to the lump sum incentive amount that he would receive after successfully selling a flat. There was a lot of money to be made quite easily if he brushed up his skills well.

Parties were very common at his new workplace after office hours. Kothari was a man of rich taste. He was an astute businessman, who knew how to influence people—be it his professional partners or his employees. Almost every alternate day, he ensured that there was a party at the office, which also happened to be the sample flat then. It started with casual get-togethers after work, where he called all his employees from the city. Then, they all started gelling well together. Pizzas were replaced with homemade food, cold drinks with alcohol and the casual parties turned into ones with a lot of insobriety and fun. But, everything should be done within a limit. When we cross that limit, problems are bound to crop up.

When Sagar had joined Kothari, he had been a small-town guy trying to find his feet in the big city—there was little work, and the area where the new complex was located had been almost empty. *The nearest locality was a little over five hundred metres away—a ten-minute walk. The area was no longer a dumping ground, but it was still deserted. The work was slow, and, apart from the labourers, no other employee had been recruited for that property. Obviously, Kothari was also handling other projects in the area, and he visited them more often because he didn't feel the need to be at a place that would be taking more time to develop, and he had entrusted the responsibility of that project to Sagar, who seemed to be a very sincere guy. Kothari had done a reference check as well and was proven right—the young small-towner with big dreams was a harmless fellow, the complete antithesis of him. Then, Sagar met Rachna.*

Rachna lived in a nearby village area—a slum. Her father provided labourers for mostly construction-related work, and Kothari was one of his important clients. Considering the importance of the project that Sagar was handling, Kothari had recommended Rachna's father to avail the best possible services. So, Rachna's father would personally inspect the premises frequently. During one of his visits, his daughter had accompanied him. Something clicked between Rachna and Sagar that afternoon, when they sat in the Sagar's office, while her father inspected the work that was being done by his labourers.

'What do you do?' Sagar asked Rachna. He wasn't too good at conversing with girls and had never ever had a friend who was a girl. But, something about Rachna reminded him of his village. It must have been her simplicity, but, apart from

that, he came to know that her family belonged to Mau, which is not very far away from Jaunpur. It's a different matter that she had never been there. Her father had moved to Mumbai before her birth, and she had never got an opportunity to visit her father's village. Sagar and Rachna had a lot in common to talk about.

'Papa tells me a lot about Jaunpur, too. He has fond memories of his school and college life,' she smiled meekly, sipping tea.

Sagar smiled back, observing that she was beautiful in a very different way and that she had long eyelashes. She looked up at him. Their eyes met. Her eyes seemed to speak to him. Sparks flew between them. They exchanged numbers before Rachna left in the evening. Thereafter, they started chatting with each other, mostly at night. They talked about everything under the sun, from Sagar's day at office to Rachna's college life, future plans, food, books, music, movies and sex. They seemed to have a lot more in common than they had thought. They began meeting on weekends and, sometimes, even on weekdays after Sagar's office hours. Rachna would pick him up on her scooty from a gully near the under-construction complex and they would head to Marve or Aksa beach. On weekends, Sagar would take her to watch the latest release in a cosy multiplex in Goregaon. It was on their third date that they began holding hands and then, they kissed on the fifth one. Before they knew it, love had blossomed and they found themselves in each other's arms between bedsheets. Sagar wanted to marry her as soon as she graduated.

'What about my career?' she asked.

'Work after we marry. But I want to be with you!' he said, planting a soft kiss on her neck.

He decided to tell his family when he travelled next to Jaunpur. These things can't be handled over the phone. His parents were conservative and would want him to opt for an arranged marriage, though Rachna's roots traced back to a nearby village and this was going to help convince them.

Dinesh Kothari learnt about Sagar and Rachna's relationship a few months later through Sagar's colleague at the property office, who had seen him with Rachna one evening.

'She is a pretty girl, no?' Dinesh's eyes lit up and he had something in mind.

'Let's have a party. A really nice one at that!'

Kothari was a family man—a dutiful husband, a good son, a responsible father—but, there was one problem. He liked to have fun outside, all sorts of fun, including parties, drinks and sex.

'Sagar, meet me in ten minutes,' Kothari called him on the way from his office in Andheri to Malad, where his blue-eyed boy worked for him.

❧

ELEVEN

The Sad Student

Kota in Rajasthan seems like a really happening place because you see students just about everywhere—young boys and girls who leave their cities, towns and villages behind and move there to better their prospects of cracking the Indian Institute of Technology's (IIT) entrance exams. The best tutorial classes in the country are apparently located in Kota. It is thought to be the place that can change the lives of many. Some crack the entrance exams in one go with flying colours, others don't do as well and don't want to settle for a second-best engineering college and still others fail miserably and keep trying. It's a good place but also one where education is a big business. It's also a place where youngsters end up winning and losing, sometimes losing way more than anyone—their mental peace, sanity and even lives.

Sanjay Bansal made a living out of the many students who came to Kota with dreams and lived there for a year, at least, sometimes more. Bansal had three houses—two of them were a stone's throw away from the best coaching institute in the city and the other was a little far away. He had been renting all these houses out to students who lived in Kota as paying guests. Needless to say, it was a continuous business. If one of them left, another student would be ready to move in the next day, in most instances. Life was good for Sanjay. He had an easy source of income without even working anywhere. All he needed to do was coordinate well with the brokers, who would help him fill up his PG accommodations.

However, Bansal had been facing some problems at one of the houses he rented out. He had contacted Raj via Facebook and invited the IPS team to Kota. He wasn't sure if they could help. In fact, he wasn't even sure if he needed IPS's help, but he just felt that it was a good decision that would be acknowledged by the six students putting up in one of his houses. It was because of them that he had to call paranormal investigators. Gaurav Tiwari was the only person he knew from the field since he had seen Gaurav on television a couple of times. It was due to the same reason that he had traced IPS and its active members.

A group of six students, five of whom had come to Kota the same year as the incident, had been residing in Bansal's third house, which was a little far away from the best coaching institute in the town. All of them went to that institute, but, since the rents were a little high in the area, they settled for a place further away. The students came from different cities and towns and had become friends within the first few days. This was the first feel of freedom for all of them, away from their parents and homes, trying their best to crack the exam that would make their lives. It was all going good for them. Until...

⟋∘

One day, Faizan, one of the boys staying in the apartment, came home a little early. Normally, after the coaching classes, the boys would go out and explore the city. But, that afternoon, Faizan just wanted to be alone. He excused himself from the group, telling them that he was feeling a little low, and returned to the empty house. Their cook—who came twice a day, once in the morning to make breakfast and lunch and then, in the late evening to cook dinner—hadn't come yet. Faizan took a bath and lazily sat in the common room, which was more like the living room of the house, though it didn't feel like one. That is where the boys watched television or played carom.

He started watching an Indian Premier League match, when he heard a knock. He turned around to look at the main door, which he had kept open. There was no one there. He turned back and resumed watching television. Close to ten minutes later, he heard a knock again. This time, it was clearer.

Faizan fearfully walked up to the main door and looked out. There was no one there, except a chaat vendor.

'Did you just knock?' Faizan asked the vendor.

The man gave him a blank look, wondering what the boy was even talking about.

Faizan thought that someone might have played a prank and run away without the vendor noticing them. So, he got back into the house and shut the door, fastening the iron latch.

He switched off the television after checking the score; his favourite team was losing the match. Studies had been bothering him as well. He had been a good student so far, but to his utter dismay and confusion, the IIT entrance exams seemed very difficult to crack. He hailed from a lower middleclass background and his parents had huge expectations from him. Obviously, most parents who send their children to Kota have high aspirations for them.

Faizan sat at his study table and opened one of the books to catch up on some homework. The boys normally did this together at night, but, with them away, Faizan decided to do it earlier for a change. He was in the midst of concentrating on his favourite subject when he heard the knock again. This time, it didn't come from the main door but his bedroom.

He was about to ask if anyone was there, although he knew that he was alone. By then, he understood that something supernatural was going on there. As he walked towards the shabby living room, every door in the house was opening and shutting on a loop and there were knocks on each door.

Faizan strode towards the main door when, suddenly, a boy's voice came from behind where Faizan had been sitting some time ago, watching the match.

'They told me I wouldn't pass,' the boy said.

Faizan turned around and saw a boy hanging from the ceiling fan in the living room.

'They told me I wouldn't pass,' he repeated, crying, looking down at Faizan, looking down with eyes that were sad but angry.

The next thing Faizan remembered was waking up with his friends sitting around him in a circle. He had blacked out after his first meeting with the dead. He knew. He believed. And it took him some time to help his friends understand that he hadn't hallucinated.

The boys called Bansal the next morning and met him at his house after the classes. Bansal, a non-believer in ghosts and hauntings, still knew that if the rumours began spreading, his business would suffer a loss. Kota was a place where such news could spread like wildfire and even brokers would not be able to help him then. The business thrived on education, sure, but also on trust. He took the responsibility of addressing this issue and contacted IPS.

∽

Meghna, Raj, Siddharth, Rith and Mohan flew in to Jaipur the next day and took a train to Kota. Thankfully, the entire team was available, which isn't always the case, as they have their own commitments and it is often difficult for all of them to make it together at such short notice. Bansal had made lodging arrangements for them at a hotel near his supposedly haunted house.

After the pre-investigation session, the team listened to Faizan patiently, as the scared boy needed a consultation. Then, the team got to the next part—attempting to communicate with the entity.

'We want to tell you one thing before we begin,' Siddharth spoke to the presence, assuming it must already be there. 'We are not here to harm you. We are here to listen to you. We are here to understand why you are still here,' he said and switched on the EMF meter first, which spiked and indicated that they were in the midst of a paranormal activity already.

'Where is the hotspot?' Siddharth asked the group of friends, who had blank expressions on their faces. They looked at Faizan, hoping he had an answer.

'Hotspot?' Faizan had no clue either.

'It means the place or places where you have witnessed most of the unnatural activities or where the presence is most intense,' Siddharth explained.

'Oh, it's the living room. That's where I saw him.'

'Where exactly?'

'Right where we are standing.'

'Oh! Oops!' Siddharth smiled. Some humour is always welcome when the team is at their job.

The room was shabby and narrow, not one bit like a living room, but the boys didn't have much choice.

Sanjay Bansal found the proceedings awkward and took their leave.

'I'll meet you in the morning,' he told them. 'Should the boys come with me tonight?' he asked Meghna.

'Not required, really. We are here. Now, if they don't want to be a part of it, they can always leave,' she informed them but observed that the friends wanted to stay back.

'Brave boys!' Raj patted them while Bansal made a move.

'We have asked the cook to not come today. We are ordering pizzas for dinner. Care for some?' one of the boys asked.

'Yes! Why not? An empty stomach and work don't go hand in hand. But we will pay for them,' Raj said.

'No! Come on, you are guests.'

'Nothing doing, boys! The dinner is on us. You treat us with some dessert. Vanilla ice-cream will do just fine,' Raj said, indicating the local ice-cream hawker who was standing on the other side of the narrow by-lane.

Once they were done with dinner and dessert and, most importantly for IPS, the group of friends were comfortable, the team opened their bags and got their equipment out. The youngsters were much intrigued by it all.

'No, no. We don't want to spoil you,' Mohan laughed as he and Rith handed over two EVP recorders—one to Siddharth and the other to Raj, who would be inspecting the premises on his own.

'Sir, IIT *mein kya rakha hain?* (What's the big deal about IIT?) We might as well join you,' one of the boys joked.

Faizan was serious, though. He knew that this was not child's play. The dead boy's face, his eyes, his voice would all be etched in Faizan's memory forever and, perhaps, a successful investigation would ensure it wouldn't trouble him the way it had then.

'Mostly, spirits keep repeating the wrong that happened to them so that others know of it. It's a form of communication, too. Disturbing, but definitely a way for them to tell you something,' Meghna had said to Faizan during a one-on-one consultation some time earlier.

By 11:00 p.m., they were all set for the night ahead. The team split up for the investigation. Siddharth and Meghna stayed at the hotspot i.e., the so-called living room where the incident had occurred. Rith and Mohan started checking the rooms while Raj went upstairs to the terrace.

Intelligent communication was established within thirty minutes at the hotspot. It was already quite evident from Faizan's experience that the entity wanted to communicate.

Siddharth initiated the session, and he continued asking the questions—mostly repeating them in different ways to get the answers they wanted.

'We want to hear your story,' Siddharth told the entity and left the EVP recorder on. Meghna clicked photographs but couldn't capture anything worth noting.

Rith and Mohan were in one of the bedrooms when the EMF meter began spiking more than it had been in the other parts of the house, except the hotspot. The team had understood that a boy who lived there earlier had died by suicide by hanging from the ceiling fan in the living room. Sanjay Bansal had informed them about it, too, because he knew it would come up. However, strangely, although the suicide had happened four years ago, none of the students who had put up at the house during this time had encountered anything that Faizan had. Bansal had even gotten a clean chit from the police station after the suicide investigation.

'The boy was depressed,' Bansal had told Meghna.

'What was his name?'

'Advik.'

'Is your name Advik? Beep once if it is,' Siddharth asked at the end of the session.

Beep!

Meanwhile, Rith attempted another EVP session in the bedroom, where the EMF meter had spiked, but he wasn't able to make any progress.

'It could be that the same entity is roaming around the house. Maybe, it was here then,' Mohan suggested.

Siddharth took some time to analyse the audio. Then, he, Meghna, Rith and Mohan joined the boys, who had been seated together in the living room, observing the process.

'Don't mind us, but paranormal investigation does not seem as interesting as they show in the movies,' one of them blurted out.

'What you see in movies is mostly exaggerated. There are times when we do get to see paranormal entities and things happen but not always,' Meghna smiled. 'Where is Raj?' she asked Rith.

'I'll get him from the terrace.'

They couldn't call him during every investigation, as they

needed to switch off their mobile phones and other electrical equipment for their devices to only pick up most genuine signals from the entities.

'But we need to call Mr Bansal,' one of the boys said, switching his phone on and dialling his number. Sanjay Bansal wasn't present with them physically, but he had told them he would not be asleep.

'Call me once this is over,' he had told the boys before leaving.

Once everyone was in the room, Siddharth began the post-investigation session, 'So, this is Advik's story.'

∽

Advik hailed from a small town in Madhya Pradesh and had been an excellent student in school—a topper who loved mathematics. An intelligent student who was passionate about studying, his claim to fame in the small town was all the coaching institute posters that he kept appearing on with a serious face. His parents were extremely proud of him, and he was that cousin in the family whose example was given to all the children. He wasn't one of those students who weren't interested in pursuing engineering and only did it because their parents pressurized them. Advik wanted to join the IIT. He was adamant about it. He knew he could crack the entrances. And then he would be all set for the future!

'Pitaji, I need to go to Kota for a year to prepare for the entrances. I have saved some money by giving tuitions and will need some more from you,' he told his parents a few days before his board exams.

'*Pehle exams toh khatam ho jaaye* (Let the exams get over first),' Advik's father responded.

'Ah, don't worry about that. I'll top it.'

Advik was so confident when it came to his studies and his future that his energy was infectious, to say the least.

Advik's parents, who wanted to be sure of finding proper accommodation for their only child, accompanied him to Kota. Advik had contacted Sanjay Bansal through Orkut and chatted with him a couple of times over the phone. Like many youngsters, this was going to be Advik's first time living away from his family, tasting freedom, understanding what it is like to be on your own. He was a little sad at first when his parents left but excited nevertheless and charged up for the future. Soon, the coaching classes commenced and he was THE student to watch out for! From the very first day, he made a terrific impression on everyone around—teachers, batchmates, roommates and even the staff at the coaching institute. He wasn't just the most brilliant student around but also the most helpful and effective communicator. Some of Advik's batchmates would meet him after the classes to clarify all their doubts, almost like a class that Advik conducted for them. In the process, he got to revise what had been taught on the day. The faculty and management at the coaching institute had high expectations from Advik and were counting on him to be one of the few students that year to make it to IIT, the best of the best. Advik was also confident he would get through.

However, a few months later, things changed drastically. He wasn't the topper he had been—his grades dropped and he was no longer the same positive and dynamic personality. He started staying aloof and grew very quiet, lost in his own world. Nobody really knew the reason because he never opened up to anyone. Some said he was high on drugs; others said they had spotted him with a girl in one of the coffee shops in a nearby area; still others were of the opinion that he had simply lost interest in studies because of the freedom, which he couldn't handle. Whatever it was, people stopped bothering about him because he didn't make a difference anymore. Students who had been envious of him felt relieved, ones who had been tutored by him after the coaching classes didn't find him helpful anymore, and his roommates were busy with their own schedules. He had no friends there. It is in such times that one understands and knows the true colours of people—the ones who are genuine and the ones who are not.

One morning, his roommates woke up to find Advik hanging from the ceiling fan in the living room.

'It was a suicide, but there were a couple of reasons behind it,' Siddharth said, moving to the next part of the post-investigation findings.

'Mr Bansal, did you know that your daughter and Advik were romantically involved?' Siddharth asked Mr Bansal over the phone.

'What are you saying?' he asked, outraged.

'Sunaina. Isn't that her name?' Siddharth asked as the

boys looked at him in wonderment.

None of them knew her name. Bansal hadn't ever discussed his daughter with the IPS team either, but they knew because Advik's spirit had communicated it to them.

'How do you—'Bansal stopped half-way through his sentence, not knowing what to say.

'It was a short-lived affair. Advik met your daughter at your house one day. Remember, you had invited him to your place?' Siddharth asked Bansal.

'Yes, I did. Once. A courier had been wrongly delivered to his address. It was nice of him to come over and give it to me.'

'Yes, Mr Bansal. Advik and Sunaina saw each other for the first time that day. Then, your daughter made the first move. She got his number from your phone and contacted him.'

It was their first love, which started with a simple friendship. They spoke over the phone, exchanged messages and chatted on Orkut. Then, one day, they decided to meet after Advik's classes. They didn't meet every day, though. Sunaina's parents never knew about it and she never wanted them to know about it either. Her family was conservative and she knew that they would think she was too young to fall in love. After all, she was their little daughter. But, she had grown up and wanted a taste of freedom too. She wanted to know what it felt like to be in love. Then, she had seen Advik. He was energetic, dynamic and there was an aura about him that was unmistakably alluring while she was shy and different. Their friendship had strong undercurrents of emotions to start with, and, soon enough, they realized that there was more to it.

One evening, one of Advik's roommates spotted him with Sunaina at a coffee shop. When the roommate asked Advik about her, he responded, 'I'll talk to Bansal ji and ask for her hand the day I get into Indian Institute of Management, Ahmedabad (IIM-A). Then, Sunaina and I can marry while I complete the course and bag a job. By then, she should be done with her studies, too.'

Bansal was unaware about his daughter's relationship. Would he have overreacted and opposed? Perhaps, yes. Perhaps, he would have told her to give it some time—let Advik pass out from IIT and get a job.

However, when it came to facing her parents to tell them that she was in a relationship with Advik, Sunaina kept procrastinating until Bansal decided his daughter's future. He was going to send her abroad to his brother's place for further studies after her boards. He knew she wasn't meant for the IITs and IIMs. He wanted the best for his daughter. After all, he had earned all his life to give her the best possible education and upbringing.

'I'm not stopping you, Sunaina. You go abroad. Study there. Do well. Meanwhile, I'll get into IIT and bag a job in a few years. Then, we can marry,' Advik said to Sunaina when she told him of her father's decision. Advik held her hands but she pulled away.

'Long-distance relationships don't work, Advik. You will find someone better,' she replied, leaving Advik in tears. Little did they both know that it would be their last meeting. The people around were looking at Advik with pity. Some even laughed. An emotional fool is always mocked.

After their breakup, Advik couldn't cope with the heartbreak because he had fallen deeply in love with Sunaina. He tried his best to get back with her, and she did meet him twice, mostly thinking that she would be able to console him and convince him about the decision she had taken. It had been for their betterment.

The breakup started affecting Advik mentally. He could not concentrate on his studies and classes, and he could not even think of a way to have Sunaina back in his life. It was a time of self-doubt, which devolved into severe complexes. Forget about people around him, he couldn't even recognize himself. What made the phase worse was his dismal performance in something he had been very proud of—his studies. There came a time when he even stopped attending the coaching classes and just sat in one corner of his room.

Depression does not discriminate between happy, sad, once-happy and once-sad people. To make matters worse, mental health problems are often ridiculed. Advik's batchmates were mostly happy to witness his downfall. Nobody cared about him or so he felt. He felt lonely and miserable, but he never called his parents to even hint about anything. How were they to know what their son was going through? Advik decided not to tell them. They expected a lot from him and had sent him to Kota to clear the IIT entrances.

He was there to make them proud. So, he tried to refocus but failed.

A few weeks before the IIT entrance exams, he mustered up the courage to be positive. He approached two of the tutors who had once been extremely proud of him and had given his example to other students.

'It's too late to catch up, but we can always try,' they told him.

He tried and they helped him by giving him extra classes. But, the truth was that Advik had somehow given up mentally. He struggled and tried to fight his inner demons but just couldn't focus. The teachers gave up on him after a week and asked him to attempt the entrance exams.

'It doesn't seem like you will pass this year. Sit for the entrances again next year,' he was told.

Everything had fallen apart for Advik. That evening, he came to know that Sunaina was going to move abroad in a week.

Unable to take it all, he ended his life that night by hanging himself from the ceiling fan in the living room.

∽

Faizan, his friends and Bansal at the other end of the phone had been listening to Siddharth as he completed Advik's story.

'But, Siddharth, why now?' Faizan asked.

'It has been quite a few years since his death and there

have been tenants who lived here before us.'

'Mr Bansal might have a better answer,' Siddharth said.

'I don't understand. Sunaina is back here after many years to get married,' Sanjay Bansal realized the reason as he responded.

'See, spirits are all around us. You might not see them. You may or may not feel them. They don't generally harm us unless there is a reason. They don't generally manifest themselves unless there is something they want to tell us,' Rith explained.

'What is it that he wants to tell us?' Bansal stammered.

Just then, Raj stormed into the room.

'Where were you? I went to the terrace to call you but you weren't there,' Rith asked.

'I was in the storeroom adjacent to it. Look what I found,' he handed over an old diary to them.

'Does Advik want this to be handed to Sunaina?' Faizan asked.

'Or simply for her to read it,' Siddharth confirmed.

In the days leading up to his suicide, Advik had mostly kept to himself and stayed indoors. He would walk up to the terrace, stroll around there, read a book or write his heart out in a diary, which he kept in the storeroom along with some of his other belongings. There wasn't enough space in his room to keep all his bags and other things. There was a small room on the terrace, and just being there, writing love letters to Sunaina, brought him some solace. He wanted her to read the letters—before or after his death. Now that she was all set for a new chapter in her life and was in Kota for a few days, he wanted to communicate to someone and tell him or her to pass on his message to Sunaina.

'Will he be at peace after this? If so, I'll inform Sunaina,' Sanjay Bansal's choked voice indicated that he was moved and disturbed after learning about what had happened. 'My daughter's intentions must have not been wrong,' he cried.

'I'm sure they weren't. But they led to a very talented boy with a very bright future ending it all. I'm not getting into whether your daughter repented or not or whether she needed to...but...' Meghna trailed off.

'Yes, Meghna. I get it. I'll talk to her in the morning. Thanks for your help, Team IPS,' Bansal said before disconnecting the line.

The group of friends were disturbed, too, after knowing about Advik.

'Boys, you are the future of the country. This is the age when a lot of things tend to happen—self-doubt, complexes, heartbreaks, distractions, and so much more. We just want to tell you that don't take this freedom for granted and simply focus on your life. Don't let petty matters hurt you or bog you down,' Meghna concluded the session as the team wrapped up.

⤛

Half-way through narrating the incidents leading up to the haunting of Meghna's house, her broker, Mr Gokhale, offered her some tea. He had understood by now that Meghna wouldn't leave without learning the whole truth.

'I have just one request, Meghna ji. Whatever you do after this, please don't drag my name into it. I don't want to get involved in any mess whatsoever,' he pleaded.

Meghna wouldn't have done this anyway. All she needed was to know the story behind the haunting at her house so that she could use the points to cleanse it.

Mr Gokhale jumped right back into his tale.

❧

After learning of Sagar's love interest, Dinesh Kothari had invited him to the office.

'Come boy, let's catch up over some drinks,' Kothari smiled and greeted Sagar, unlocking the door of his car for Sagar, who got in and shook hands.

'Where are we going, Sir?'

'Some nice and quiet bar where we can talk.'

Real estate is one of those industries that can get really dirty—there is a lot of money at stake, money which is there to be spent not only on the construction and other work-related matters but also on the avenues from where the real work is obtained. Permits, licenses and a lot of other things—it's a sector ridden with corrupt practices. Land purchases, registrations, permissions to build, even selling constructed properties all entail bribes at every step. Kothari had to pay off officials in government agencies to finish the project and he had to stay on the right side of local politicians.

Yash Chaudhari was one such local politician. He belonged to an influential but infamous family in the area. Yash's grandfather was a former underworld gangster who had been imprisoned several times in smuggling, murder and land grab cases. His father was a politician and chairman of a regional political party. Yash operated as a local politician and assisted his father. Due to the grandfather's immense influence in certain areas of the city and, quite obviously, because of their criminal background, Yash's father's political party as well as the family business, Sapna Group (named after Yash's mother), completely controlled and monitored many of the construction projects in the city. People like Kothari survived and sustained because of this family. This meant that Kothari kept the family as happy as he could in every way.

Yash was going to turn nineteen in a few days. Knowing what a spoilt brat Yash was, Kothari wanted to throw a big party for him. There would be food, drinks and, of course, girls. It was to be a high socialite party to initiate Yash into manhood. Kothari was planning to invite some big people to the party, but he also wanted Sagar to be there with Rachna. She was a sweet and young girl who could be Yash's date that night. Moreover, since Sagar knew her well, he could convince her to spend some quality time with the to-be-man. Nobody would know. In turn, Kothari would take good care of Sagar's career.

'I know all of this because of my contacts, Ma'am. I don't know what happened at the party. Yes, Sagar and the girl were nowhere to be seen after that party. Some tell me there were murders that night. A few guests have been missing, too, apart from those two. The police were bribed by Yash and Kothari—the cases didn't come to light at all,' Mr Gokhale concluded.

'Thank you. I think I can take care of it from here,' Meghna stood up to leave.

'Ma'am, please do remember your promise,' Mr Gokhale pleaded one last time.

By the time Meghna reached home, it was noon. She called Siddharth the moment she got home.

'Sid, I'll need you for this one. Can you come over in the evening?' Meghna asked.

She knew two things by now. One, she was not going to investigate this case on her own. Two, the spirits in the house were furious. She needed Siddharth's expertise. Rith and Mohan were not in the city. Raj lived in Delhi, and this was not a professional case. She was dealing with ghosts in her own house!

'Yeah, I'll be there,' Siddharth responded, just waking up.

'Oh and, yes! Bring some burgers and Coke, will you?'

'Ah, of course! Happy weekend!'

While waiting for Siddharth to get to their house, Meghna discussed the case with her mother, Ekta, Gautam and everyone in the family. She told them about what she had heard from Mr Gokhale.

'I normally don't suggest this to clients, but I think you all should not be here in the house tonight. This might be more *dangerous than we think,' she told them.*

'Megs, when you are here with us, we have no reason to worry. We are not leaving you, baby. We will stay silent in one of the rooms while you and Siddharth investigate,' Meghna's mother asserted adamantly. She was confident nothing would happen to them with Meghna around. She was certain that her daughter was one hell of a strong woman!

Siddharth reached the house at around 4:00 p.m.

'All set?' were his first words as Meghna let him in.

'Now we are! We didn't cook today. So, let's have our fill and get to work,' Meghna cheered.

'Yo!' Siddharth smiled.

Meghna's knowledge about the tragic incident would help them cleanse the house, or so she thought. Mr Gokhale had told her whatever he knew and Meghna tried to guess the possibilities of what may have happened that night.

It could be that Sagar had invited Rachna to the party on Kothari's request and something wrong had happened to both of them along with a few other guests.

It could also be that Sagar had sold his soul and compromised on his ethics, invited Rachna to the party and handed her over to Kothari and Yash for the night. Something wrong must have happened, if this was true too.

Whatever it was, Meghna was sure that the wrongs committed during Yash's birthday party were causing the haunting—spirits of the wronged caught in a loop, trying to undo what happened to them but, obviously, failing at their attempts. Were they harmful? No. But, if the inhabitants of the house came between their activities, they could be.

Meghna had her family stay in one of the rooms and asked them to stay silent. The cleansing could take hours and the least possible interference would help expedite the process.

Meghna and Siddharth got to work around 8:00 p.m. Paranormal investigators listen to the spirits—their painful stories and why they are still where they are. Empathy always helps, be it for the living or the dead. Communication helps establish a proper balance between the physical world and the other world.

'See, we have an idea about the cause of the haunting. But, since the spirits here are in no mood to talk to us or perhaps we are yet to understand if they are, we need to resort to holy water, burning sage and spreading salt around the perimeter of the house,' Siddharth suggested while getting all their equipment out.

Once they were done with the basic requirements, Meghna lit a few candles and lanterns, placed them in various parts of the house and switched off the lights. While she started taking photographs of various nooks and corners, Siddharth sat in the living room and attempted an EVP session.

It was not before 11:00 p.m. that they sensed some activity. It began in the kitchen.

'We know you might be hearing us but don't want to. If you change your mind, we want to tell you that we are here to listen to you,' Siddharth said. Meghna joined him and repeated.

'We are here to help—'

CRACK! Meghna and Siddharth's attempts to communicate were interrupted by the loud noise of the large mirror in the living room cracking. *The sound pierced through their ears and a gust of wind swept across the house, blowing the candles out, leaving them dependent on the lanterns, that too for just a minute. One by one, all the lanterns started to burst while Meghna and Siddharth stood there in horror.*

They still mustered up courage and asked, 'Is there anything you want to tell us?'

They started hearing the sound of the violin playing, accompanied by a group of people chatting among themselves and the clinking of glasses and cutlery.

'We repeat. Please communicate!' Meghna screamed this time.

'We repeat. Please communicate!' a lady's voice mimicked her, and the very next moment, they saw the lady in the white gown appear in front of their eyes and disappear within a moment.

'Please don't...Please don't!' a young girl's voice echoed through the house.

BANG! A gunshot!

Siddharth and Meghna took as many photographs as possible, using their night vision cameras.

'What the hell happened here?' Meghna shrieked.

'Turns out it's an intelligent haunting, Meghna,' Siddharth whispered.

And then, the spirits manifested themselves as orbs—transparent balls, like globes of light or energy, that are connected with spirits. The free-floating balls of light were all around them, often flashing very brightly.

'We... we know you are in a lot of pain here. Whatever happened here was wrong. The people responsible for the crimes should be punished, but, please understand, we are not them. We are here to try and listen to you since we can. We would suggest you to leave this place or, at least, not cross boundaries. We will not harm you either,' Meghna pleaded.

This is when both Siddharth and Meghna heard a familiar voice. It came from the mirror, the one that had cracked some time back.

'Gaurav?' they both said at the same time as their mentor's spirit called them from the other side of the mirror—the other world.

All they could see was another orb flashing even brighter than the others, as if it wanted to convey to them that it was Gaurav.

'They will not harm you, Meghna,' Gaurav said to them.

Meghna and Siddharth broke down. Gaurav had been watching over them, like a guardian angel, all this time. He had never left them. He had never given up on them. He had known that they would continue living his dream and vision after his death.

'Please, always continue to look after us, Sir,' Siddharth said.

'Remember the souvenirs I collected and at times, ghosts followed me to our office? It works. Each of you have something that once belonged to me. I must have gifted you or just given you. Take care of them. I'm always there,' his deep voice reverberated around the room. 'And let me tell you what I'm doing here. I continue with my research to know more about the...UNKNOWN! It's just that I'm doing it from this side of the spectrum now. Take care, folks!'

All the orbs disappeared at once. Everything suddenly seemed normal. The temperature, which had dropped while the haunting had been happening, normalized, indicating that the haunting had ended. Meghna opened the door of the room where her family had been spending the night.

'Is it over?' Meghna's mother asked, quite sure that her daughter had added another feather in her cap.

'Mom, there is nothing to worry. He is with us,' Meghna smiled and hugged her.

Siddharth wiped his tears and looked around, hoping Gaurav could see him.

'Thank you for everything,' he whispered.

❧

Team Members of Indian Paranormal Society

Waqar Raj is one of the founding members, technical head and head of operations of the IPS. His extensive research and excellent technical knowledge make him the best in the field. Professionally, he's an entrepreneur and has been investigating the paranormal since 2012. He has successfully documented some of the most ground-breaking evidence about the paranormal.

Siddharth Bantval is a paranormal/metaphysical researcher at the IPS. He has been researching the paranormal since 2014 and has successfully collected suggestive evidence of the paranormal. He's also a certified psychological counsellor and is keenly interested in parapsychology. In his work, he brings the perfect amalgamation of his theoretical knowledge of the paranormal with his field investigations.

Meghna Porwal has been a paranormal investigator at the IPS since 2015. She specializes in capturing photographic anomalies. She's also known for her unique techniques to gather evidence of the paranormal. She's one of the best female paranormal investigators the country has ever seen.

Rith Deb has been an investigator at the IPS since 2014. His childhood encounters with the unknown turned him into a believer and led him to the IPS. In his approach to the paranormal, he strikes the perfect balance between belief and scepticism. He has contributed greatly to documenting evidence of the paranormal.

Mohan Kattimani is a seaman by profession and a paranormal investigator by passion. He is the team's equipment manager and ensures that all of IPS's equipment is taken care of and functional before any investigation. He also helps in evidence analysis and review. Mohan is an integral part of the IPS and has been responsible for carrying out our operations in Europe and the USA.

Glossary

Entity: Any haunting that shows some semblance of a living being (it could be through shape, sound or any other form/interaction).

Ghost: An entity that resembles a human.

Spirit: The ghost of a once-living person with non-physical attributes, like emotions and personality.

Poltergeist: This term originates from the German words 'polter' meaning 'noisy' and 'geist' meaning 'ghost'. It is believed to be a type of spirit/ghost that is responsible for physical disturbances, such as loud and objects being moved or destroyed.

Devil/inhuman entities: These entities are believed to not have experienced life in the way we humans have. They are believed to be negative, and their only goal is to disrupt the lives of other beings.

Haunting: The act of something or someone repeatedly

visiting a place, thought or memory. Something that recurs persistently, disturbing the normal pattern of life—a reported activity that could be paranormal.

Anomaly: Something that is abnormal, peculiar or not easily classified. Anomalies are parts of the documentation/recordings done by paranormal researchers as part of their research.

Paranormal investigation: This is a process of research, investigation and evidence collection undertaken by paranormal investigators in a place that their client claims is haunted. Documentation of changes in the ambient environment is a critical part of a paranormal investigation. This sometimes includes anomalies that may (after intensive analysis) turn into potential evidence that shares a strong link with the paranormal.

Electronic voice phenomena (EVP): These are sounds documented on digital audio or analogue voice recorders believed to be sourced by ghosts, spirits, entities, etc. The documentation of this anomaly or sound is known as an EVP.

Digital audio recorder (EVP recorder): Audio recording equipment used to document EVP (and audio anomalies).

Full spectrum camera: Cameras that are used by paranormal researchers to photograph/video record in the night without an external light source. They are a specialized piece of equipment that captures pictures using broadband/full-spectrum film, which is visible and near-infrared light, commonly referred to as the 'VNIR'. The human eye can only see in a particular spectrum of light; however, a full spectrum camera can document in any and every spectrum of light, ranging from infrared to ultraviolet.

Night vision camera/infrared camera: These are photographic/video documentation devices used by paranormal researchers to photograph/videotape anomalies at night without an external light source. Infrared light is electromagnetic radiation (EMR) that has a longer wavelength than those of visible light, which, therefore, cannot be seen by the human eye.

Tri-field meter/Tri-axis field meter: This is an Electromagnetic field (EMF) measuring device that has a three-axis sensor. It is a single unit that combines all the features needed for fast, accurate measurements of EMF and radio frequencies.

Electromagnetic frequency/electromagnetic fields: EMF travel through space, carrying electromagnetic radiant energy. It includes radio waves, microwaves, infrared and ultraviolet light, X-rays and gamma rays. They are commonly sourced from household electric equipment, mobile phones, walkie-talkies, etc. Paranormal researchers usually document changes in EMF when all the household equipment is turned off and the ambient environment is void of radiations sourced from the above-mentioned devices.

EMF/K-II meter: This is a piece of specialized equipment that helps document EMF that may be sourced by household equipment, walkie-talkies, mobile towers, unknown source like ghosts, spirits, energies, etc. They are also used in industries to check for any electrical leakages in machinery and other equipment.

Intelligent haunting: This is a type of haunting where the presence, ghost, spirit or entity communicates or responds in a way that correlates to something of significance to the paranormal researcher/subject of research.

Residual haunting: This is a type of haunting based on the Stone Tape theory. It is synonymous to tape recordings, where an event gets recorded and stored in objects that are available in that space. They are more of mental impressions that are captured or trapped in a space where the people who had resided or had been present there may have experienced a traumatic event. It is believed that emotional energy or memories can be captured within a space and may replay the event over and over again under certain conditions.

Possession: A phenomena where a subject/person under the influence of something results in a change of behaviour and overall personality. Paranormal researchers believe that some spirits or ghosts can influence people or subjects.

Object manipulation: A phenomena where objects move or displace on their own without a human agent interfering with them or applying any force. It is believed that ghosts or spirits can psychokinetically move objects.

Hotspots: A place where most of the paranormal activities in a space are focussed. These spots are marked by paranormal researchers to document or record anomalous activities using their equipment.

Cleansing: This is an activity performed by paranormal researchers or spiritual healers to help a subject or client rid a place of unwanted energies or to help a human agent get rid of any kind of attachment or possession. Different techniques are used by researchers or healers to perform the cleansing.

Out of body experience (OBE): A sensation or experience of being outside one's body, similar to floating or flying, while being able to observe themselves (their biological body) from a distance.

Astral projection: Like an OBE, this is believed to be experienced by individuals with much practice of the art of travelling to the other world, wherein the subject can intentionally separate their consciousness, spirit or soul from their physical body.

Near death experience (NDE): An unusual experience, where a person or subject is on the brink of death (at times declared clinically dead by medical professionals), but, under unknown circumstances, the person comes back to life with varied memories of what happened in the duration of being declared dead and coming back to life. Medical professionals have a different outlook on this experience whereas paranormal researchers believe it is similar to an OBE.